INSTRUCTOR'S MANUAL

THIRD EDITION
PHYSICS

INTRODUCTION

This instructor's resource manual is designed to accompany the third edition of *Physics* by John D. Cutnell and Kenneth W. Johnson (John Wiley & Sons, 1994), a book that contains 32 chapters and is intended for the course usually referred to as *College Physics*, a course that assumes that students have a knowledge of algebra and are familiar with simple relations from trigonometry.

For each chapter of the text, this resource manual contains the following:

A list of **Transparencies (acetates)** for the chapter. These are four-color transparencies made from selected diagrams (figures) in the text. The number per chapter ranges from seven to fourteen; there are a total of 300 transparencies.

Solved Problems. This is a list of problems in the chapter that are solved in detail in the *Study Guide with Selected Solutions* by Mark Comella, Charles R. McKenzie, and Andrew J. Pica in collaboration with the authors of the primary text. The *Study Guide* is keyed to the text and is intended to be of assistance in encouraging and motivating students and in helping them develop problem solving skills.

Spreadsheets suitable for use by students in studying the material in the particular chapter. These refer to the supplement *Wondering About Physics...Using Spreadsheets to Find Out* by Dewey I. Dykstra, Jr. and Robert G. Fuller (John Wiley & Sons, 1988).

Demonstrations appropriate for material in the chapter. Each chapter has references to demonstrations selected from four well known demonstration resource books (see subsequent section for details). In addition, for most chapters I have given instructions for performing a few relatively simple demonstrations that I have found to be effective.

Films are listed for almost all chapters. As used here, "films" include 16mm films, filmstrips, videocassettes, and laser discs. The format, length, and source of each film is shown; addresses of sources are given in a separate compilation.

Laboratory experiments for almost every chapter were selected from two laboratory manuals published by John Wiley. These are: *Laboratory Experiments in College Physics*, Seventh Edition, by Cicero H. Bernard and Chirold D. Epp and *Experiments in Physics* by Daryl W. Preston, Joseph W. Kane, and Morton W. Sternheim. The first manual is a comprehensive one containing 52 experiments; the second manual features 27 experiments of which more than a third have a biological science emphasis.

INSTRUCTOR'S MANUAL

ROBERT LEE KERNELL
Old Dominion University

THIRD EDITION
PHYSICS

JOHN D. CUTNELL
KENNETH W. JOHNSON
Southern Illinois University at Carbondale

 John Wiley & Sons, Inc.
New York Chichester
Brisbane Toronto Singapore

ISBN 0-471-04057-6

Printed in the United States of America

10 9 8 7 6 5 4 3 2 1

Printed and bound by Malloy Lithographing, Inc.

CONTENTS

Introduction 2

Textbook Conversion Notes: Discussion 5

Table for Textbook Conversion 7

Comparing 2nd ed. and 3rd ed. of Cutnell and Johnson 11

Demonstrations 14

Key to Film Sources 16

Computers 19

Key to Computer Resources 22

Suggested Courses and Sample Schedules 24

Ideas for the First Time Lecturer 29

Teaching Aids and Lecture Notes for Each Chapter 47

Problem Locator Guide 267

Computer Resources suitable for the chapter. The nature of the listings under this category is described in detail in a subsequent section. This section draws heavily on the Instructor's Manual prepared by J. Richard Christman for use with the classic *Fundamentals of Physics* calculus level text by Halliday, Resnick, and Walker (John Wiley 1993). Appreciation is expressed to Dr. Christman (and to John Wiley, Publishers) for permission to use this material.

Lecture Notes are given for each chapter. These are presented in outline form and consist largely of the main and secondary headings of the various sections in each chapter of the text. Generous space is allowed on the outline so that each instructor can make his/her own detailed outline according to individual preferences. For most chapters the Lecture Notes are three pages long. An additional page, entitled **Next Time Notes** is included following the Lecture Notes. This may be helpful for making notes on (1) what went well with various items (demonstrations, examples, films, etc) and (2) anything else that you may want to remember for next time.

In addition to the resources listed with the individual chapters, this manual contains several items of a more general nature. These are:

Textbook Conversion Notes. These notes compare the coverage of topics in the book by Cutnell and Johnson with that of six other books that are rather widely used as texts in College Physics courses. This section is intended to assist physics instructors in considering texts for adoption for their classes and in converting their lecture notes from one text to another.

Suggested Courses. Syllabi used in College Physics classes on a variety of campuses throughout the nation have been examined with a view to preparing a suggested schedule appropriate for a one-year course given under either the semester or the quarter system. Discussion is given regarding allocation of lecture time to the 32 chapters in the text.

Ideas for the First Time Lecturer. The then (1988) Physics Editor of John Wiley insisted that I write several pages that purport to be "what an experienced and successful College Physics instructor would relate to a colleague teaching the course for the first time." Her insistence and my persistence have resulted in the seventeen pages of jottings that constitute this section of the resource manual.

Several additional supplements that are coordinated with the text are available. These are:

Solutions Manual by Mark Comella, Charles R. McKenzie, and Andrew J. Pica. This manual is available only to instructors; it contains detailed solutions to all problems in the text in a form suitable for posting or for preparing transparencies to use in class or review sessions.

Solutions Disk, a computer disk version of the *Solutions Manual* is available in Word Perfect or Microsoft Word format.

Test Bank by David Marx and Mark Comella, contains more than 1500 short answer questions and problems.

Computerized Test Bank (Brownstone Testing Service) consists of IBM, Apple II, and Macintosh versions of the entire Test Bank with full editing features to help you customize your tests.

Homework Disk contains material similar to (and includes some material from) *Computerized Test Bank* as well as other material that is useful in assigning and grading homework. This disk will be especially useful in connection with homework for large classes.

As you can see, an impressive set of supplements is available to support the primary text. I hope that this instructor's resource manual will be useful to those who struggle to enlighten today's generation of students about physics. It has been a pleasure to work with Joan Kalkut, Supplements Editor, and Catherine Donovan, Administrative Assistant, at John Wiley, Publishers. I appreciate the good work done by Dennis E. Ray in word processing and formatting. I am very much indebted to all my physics colleagues at Old Dominion University for many helpful discussions (including a few heated arguments!) pertaining to physics in general and to teaching physics in particular.

R L Kernell

Robert Lee Kernell
Old Dominion University
Norfolk, Virginia 23529-0116
May 20, 1994

TEXTBOOK CONVERSION NOTES: DISCUSSION

This section compares the topic coverage in the 3rd edition of Cutnell and Johnson with that in six other textbooks that are rather widely used in college physics courses having a prerequisite of algebra and some trigonometry. This comparison will be useful to those choosing a text for such a course. The books compared are:

TITLE	AUTHORS	CODE
Physics (3rd ed.)	Cutnell and Johnson	C/J
Physics (3rd ed.)	Giancoli	G
Physics	Hecht	H
Contemporary College Physics (2nd ed.)	Jones and Childers	J/C
Principles of Physics	Ohanian	O
College Physics (3rd ed.)	Serway and Faughn	S/F
College Physics (2nd ed.)	Wilson	W

After giving a general overview of these texts, we will present a detailed list of topics together with the specific pages on which each topic is covered in these seven books.

The subject matter in all of these books is divided into six sections:
mechanics
thermal physics
wave motion and sound
electricity and magnetism
light and optics
modern physics

In most institutions, the first three sections are covered in the first semester and the latter three sections in the second semester. There is complete uniformity among these five books in the allocation of broad topics to a given semester. There are, of course, differences in which particular topics are covered within each section and, to some extent, in the particular section in which a given topic is discussed. For example, some authors include simple harmonic motion in the mechanics section; others treat SHM in the wave motion and sound section. There is also a variation in the sequence in which the various sections are presented. For example, some books place thermal physics after mechanics and conclude the first semester material with wave motion and sound. Other books reverse the order in which thermal physics and wave motion (including sound) are covered. Almost all college physics textbooks present the second semester material in the sequence: electricity and magnetism, light and optics, and modern physics. Here, again, there are differences in the ordering of topics within a given section.

In previous editions of this Instructor's Manual, we have presented a rather detailed discussion of the differences in coverage for four texts in addition to Cutnell/Johnson. Now that textbook conversion information embraces C/J and six other books, such a discussion of differences in coverage would quickly become tedious and probably of limited usefulness. Hence we will present a list of topics and corresponding page references. Those who have a particular interest in what topic is covered in what order in what section in which book can deduce the desired information from the list of topics and pages. Toward this end, the table beginning on the next page presents a list of topics and indicates the pages on which each topic is discussed in each of the seven books. For the convenience of those presently using Cutnell/Johnson as a text, a second table lists the topics and page numbers for the 2nd and 3rd editions of C/J.

TABLE FOR TEXTBOOK CONVERSION

This table presents a listing of topics and the pages on which these topics are covered in the following seven textbooks:

Physics (3rd ed.)	Cutnell and Johnson	**C/J**
Physics (3rd ed.)	Giancoli	**G**
Physics	Hecht	**H**
Contemporary College Physics (2nd ed.)	Jones and Childers	**J/C**
Principles of Physics	Ohanian	**O**
College Physics (3rd ed.)	Serway and Faughn	**S/F**
College Physics (2nd ed.)	Wilson	**W**

TOPIC	C/J	G	H	J/C	O	S/F	W
MECHANICS:							
Introduction, Units	1-8	1-15	1-14	1-27	1-7	1-10	1-31
Mathematics, Scalars, and Vectors	9-28	43-52	14-22 32-35 44-49	57-69	55-59	11-25 51-57	70-79
Kinematics in One Dimension	29-61	15-42	23-75	28-56	7-38	26-50	32-64
Kinematics in Two Dimensions	62-86	53-64 97-99	75-82	69-86	39-77	57-73	65-70 79-100
Newton's Laws of Motion	87-97	65-73	89-101 125-130	87-102	78-89	74-83	101-114 120-123
The Gravitational Force	97-102	106-109	207-238	142-150	159-183	184-195	226-241
Application of Newton's Laws	102-136	74-96	130-139 146-173	103-127	90-122	84-107	114-120 123-137
Uniform Circular Motion	137-158	100-123	139-146 218-227	131-142	63-65 110-113	177-183	207-222
Work, Energy, and Power	159-195	124-148	277-316	156-186	123-158	108-140	138-171
Impulse and Momentum	196-218	149-172	101-117	187-216	184-218	141-169	172-206
Rotational Kinematics	219-242	173-177	239-250	229-234	219-227	170-176	222-226
Torque, Rotational Equilibrium	243-255	178-180 205-217	173-193	234-242	250-273	211-218	252-264

TOPIC	C/J	G	H	J/C	O	S/F	W
MECHANICS: (continued)							
Rotational Dynamics	255-278	181-204	250-268	246-266	228-249	219-244	265-291
Elements; Properties of Matter	279-285	218-227	317-351	242-245	262-265	247-255	292-298
Simple Harmonic Motion	285-313	274-284	401-419	379-404	274-300	421-437	422-435
Fluid Statics	314-330	237-247	353-374	267-280	353-361	255-277	299-314
Fluid Dynamics	330-359	248-272	374-399	281-297	346-353 361-379	278-301	315-332
THERMAL PHYSICS:							
Temperature, Thermal Expansion	360-374	337-345	481-494	298-308	386-390 406-411	312-321	333-319
Calorimetry and Phase Changes	374-398	370-378	513-534	308-315	402-406 414-415	342-352	360-375
Transfer of Heat	399-421	379-390	534-540	315-319	411-413	353-368	375-386
Ideal Gas Law, Kinetic Theory	422-444	347-369	494-506	324-346	380-386 415-419	322-341	349-354
Thermodynamics Law I	445-456	391-394	549-570	351-366	427-437	369-377	392-400
Thermodynamics Law II	456-481	395-415	570-585	367-378	437-451	378-401	400-421
WAVE MOTION AND SOUND:							
Introduction to Waves	482-489	286-307	420-433	405-410	301-306	437-454	435-439
Sound, Doppler Effect	489-520	308-336	442-480	410-419	320-345	458-494	454-481
Superposition, Interference	521-547	296-301	458-469	419-429	306-319	433-445 471-480	440-453

TOPIC	C/J	G	H	J/C	O	S/F	W
ELECTRICITY AND MAGNETISM:							
Electric Forces and Fields	548-584	416-439	587-624	435-463	452-500	501-534	482-501
Electric Potential, Capacitance	585-612	440-458	625-659	464-490	501-534	535-568	501-517
Electric Current, Resistance, Power	614-628	459-479	661-688	491-504	535-555	569-588	518-538
Electric Circuits	628-643	480-504	689-720	504-524	556-583	592-622	539-569
Series and Parallel Capacitors	643-647	488-491	643-650	512-514	519-522	548-552	510-512
Magnetic Fields	569-702	505-537	721-762	525-555	584-618	626-659	570-600
Electromagnetic Induction	704-743	538-554	763-794	556-580	619-644	660-689	601-631
Alternating Current Circuits	744-767	555-570	795-832	581-600	645-665	695-718	632-650
Semiconductor Devices	756-763	790-795	818-824	884-894	851-855	997-1002	
LIGHT AND OPTICS:							
Electromagnetic Waves	768-791	571-588	833-861	572-575 602-604	666-691	719-742	618-626
Reflection	793-795	592-593	867-873	604-606	695-697	754-755	652-654
Mirrors	795-815	594-600	925-931	622-625	705-709	779-787	672-685
Refraction	816-831	589-591 601-602	873-882	606-610	697-705	755-763 767-778	654-671
Lenses	831-839	605-619	893-910	611-621 625-633	709-712	788-808	685-702
Optical Instruments	839-865	654-684	910-925	634-654	712-728	840-870	735-766
Wave Nature of Light	866-901	620-653	939-978	655-690	729-756	809-839	703-734
Color			882-885	862-870		763-766	757-759

10

TOPIC	C/J	G	H	J/C	O	S/F	W
MODERN PHYSICS:							
Special Relativity	902-925	685-718	979-1014	691-726	757-785	876-904	767-799
Particles and Waves	926-945	719-730	1015-1025 1043-1056	728-744 762-781	786-809	913-942	800-810 826-830
The Nature of the Atom	946-980	731-775	1028-1041 1056-1100	757-762 771-791	810-846	946-979	810-824 830-848
Molecular Bonding, Band Theory		776-789		872-884	846-851	984-996	
Nuclear Physics, Radioactivity	981-1006	800-851	1025-1028 1101-1136	744-752 814-830	861-880	1008-1064	849-881
Ionizing Radiation, Nuclear Energy, and Elementary Particles	1007-1031	852-877	1123-1131 1137-1164	831-848 900-917	880-915	1065-1091	882-906

COMPARISON OF TOPIC COVERAGE
2nd ed. and 3rd ed. of *Physics* by Cutnell and Johnson

For the convenience of those presently using the second edition of this text by Cutnell and Johnson, the table below lists topics and pages on which the topics are covered in the second and third editions.

TOPIC	C/J-2	C/J-3
MECHANICS:		
Introduction, Units	1-8	1-8
Mathematics, Scalars, Vectors	9-26	9-28
Kinematics in One Dimension	27-56	29-61
Kinematics in Two Dimensions	57-77	62-86
Newton's Laws of Motion	78-88	87-97
The Gravitational Force	89-93	97-102
Application of Newton's Laws	94-124	102-136
Uniform Circular Motion	125-144	137-158
Work, Energy, and Power	145-173	159-195
Impulse and Momentum	174-193	196-218
Rotational Kinematics	194-214	219-242
Torque, Rotational Equilibrium	215-225	243-255
Rotational Dynamics	226-247	255-278
Elasticity; Properties of Matter	248-257	279-285
Simple Harmonic Motion	258-279	285-313

TOPIC	C/J-2	C/J-3
MECHANICS: (continued)		
Fluid Statics	280-295	314-330
Fluid Dynamics	296-322	330-359
THERMAL PHYSICS:		
Temperature, Thermal Expansion	323-336	360-374
Calorimetry, Phase Changes	337-360	374-398
Transfer of Heat	361-380	399-421
Ideal Gas Law, Kinetic Theory	381-400	422-444
Thermodynamics Law I	401-411	445-456
Thermodynamics Law II	412-437	456-481
WAVE MOTION AND SOUND:		
Introduction to Waves	438-444	482-489
Sound, Doppler Effect	445-472	489-520
Superposition, Interference	473-497	521-547
ELECTRICITY AND MAGNETISM:		
Electric Forces and Fields	498-527	548-584
Electric Potential, Capacitance	528-552	585-612
Electric Current, Resistance, Power	553-565	614-628
Electric Circuits	566-594	628-658
Series and Parallel Capacitors	580-582	643-647

TOPIC	C/J-2	C/J-3
ELECTRICITY AND MAGNETISM: (continued)		
Magnetic Fields	595-633	659-702
Electromagnetic Induction	634-671	704-743
Alternating Current Circuits	672-682	744-767
Semiconductor Devices	683-689	756-763
LIGHT AND OPTICS:		
Electromagnetic Waves	694-715	768-791
Reflection	716-718	793-795
Mirrors	719-733	795-815
Refraction	734-747	816-831
Lenses	748-763	831-839
Optical Instruments	764-780	839-865
Wave Nature of Light	781-813	866-901
MODERN PHYSICS:		
Special Relativity	814-836	902-925
Particles and Waves	837-853	926-945
The Nature of the Atom	854-883	946-980
Nuclear Physics, Radioactivity	884-907	981-1006
Ionizing Radiation, Nuclear Energy, and Elementary Particles	908-929	1007-1031

DEMONSTRATIONS

There are several excellent books on demonstrations suitable for the introductory physics course. For each chapter of the text, the TEACHING AIDS page of this resource manual lists some demonstrations from the following four books:

The Dick and Rae Physics Demo Book, D. Rae Carpenter, Jr. and Richard B. Minnix, 1993. The authors, professors of physics at Virginia Military Institute, are nationally acclaimed physics demonstrators. Available from Dick and Rae, Inc., Lexington, VA 24450-0304.

A Demonstration Handbook for Physics, G.D. Freier and F.J. Anderson, 320 pages, 1981. Contains instructions (with line drawings) for 807 demonstrations, many of which can be set up using simple equipment. Available from American Association of Physics Teachers, One Physics Ellipse, College Park, MD 20740-3845.

Physics Demonstration Experiments at William Jewell College, Wallace A. Hilton, 112 pages, 1982. More than 300 demonstrations are described. Available from AAPT at the address given above.

Physics Demonstration Experiments, Harry F. Meiners, ed. Published in 1970. This two-volume work of more than 1300 pages is an excellent source of information on specific demonstrations as well as general articles that discuss the philosophy and techniques of lecture demonstrations. Available from Robert E. Krieger Publishing Company, Malabar, FL 32950.

Other publications and books that are useful are:

Resource Letter PhD-1: Physics Demonstrations, J.A. Davis and B.G. Eaton, 6 pages, 1979. Has 103 references to books and monographs that deal with physics demonstrations. Available from AAPT at the address given above.

Apparatus for Teaching Physics, reprinted from *The Physics Teacher*, American Association of Physics Teachers, 1972.

Apparatus Notes, reprinted from *American Journal of Physics*, 1965-72, American Association of Physics Teachers, 1972.

Demonstration Experiments in Physics, Richard M. Sutton, McGraw-Hill, New York, 1938. Now available as a reprint from AAPT.

Demonstrations in Physics, Julius Sumner Miller, Ure Smith, London, 1969.

Experiments and Demonstrations in Optics, C. Harvey Palmer, Johns Hopkins University Press, Baltimore, 1962.

Exploring Laser Light, T. Kallard. Available from AAPT at address given above, 1977.

Phenomenal Physics, Clifford E. Swartz, John Wiley, New York, 1981.

Physics Demonstrations and Experiments for High School, Gordon E. Jones, Physics Department, Mississippi State University, Mississippi State, MS 39762

Turning the World Inside Out, Robert Ehrlich, Princeton University Press, Princeton N.J., 1990

All of these books or articles on demonstrations are worth having in your office. My own particular favorites are the 1938 classic by Richard Sutton (late of California Institute of Technology), the 1993 book by Rae Carpenter and Dick Minnix, and the 1990 book by Robert Ehrlich (George Mason University). This latter book contains 175 illustrations and is as unusual as its title in that many of the demonstrations are performed on an overhead projector. Whatever your favorite demonstration books may be, I hope that you will weave some demonstrations into your lectures.

In the last few years several excellent collections of demonstrations and instructional materials have become available on laserdiscs or videocassettes. An excellent source of short demonstrations on video discs is **PHYSICS: CINEMA CLASSICS**. This disc contains extensive extracts from the PSSC film series, the Project Physics films, Ealing 8mm film loops, and several other sources. AAPT has recently produced full-color videos of three classic film loop series (Harvard Project Physics, Ealing, and Franklin Miller, Jr.) by transferring the film loop versions onto VHS videocassettes. Audio tracks and sound effects have been included. *THE MECHANICAL UNIVERSE* consists of 52 half-hour segments covering most topics in introductory physics; order this from The Mechanical Universe, Caltech, MS 1-70, Pasadena, CA 91125. A comprehensive source of demonstrations is the 25 laserdisc set *The Video Encyclopedia of Physics Demonstrations*. Write The Education Group, Inc., 1235 Sunset Plaza Drive, Los Angeles, CA 90069.

For further information on what is available, write:
    AAPT Instructional Materials Center
    One Physics Ellipse
    College Park, MD 20740-3845

Contact this center (301) 209-3300 for up-to-date information on the uses of state-of-the-art technologies in the teaching of physics.

KEY TO FILM SOURCES

AAPT	American Association of Physics Teachers One Physics Ellipse, College Park, MD 20740-3845
ACAY	Academy Films Box 1023, Venice, CA 90291
AEF	American Educational Films 132 Lasky Dr., P.O. Box 5001 Beverly Hills, CA 90212
AIMS	Aims Distribution Media Services, Inc. P.O. Box 1010, Hollywood, CA 90028
BAY	Around the Bay 1140 Irving St., San Francisco, CA 94122
BFA	BFA Educational Media Div. Of Columbia Broadcasting System 2211 Michigan Ave., P.O. Box 1795 Santa Monica, CA 90406
BTL	Bell Telephone Laboratories Film Library, Murray Hill, N.J. 07971
CEC	Centron Educational Films, Centron Corp. P.O. Box 687, Lawrence, KS 66044
CENCO	Cenco Educational Films (Out of Business) (Rent through university distribution center.)
CHUH	Churchill Films 662 N. Robertson Blvd., Los Angeles, CA 90069
CORONET	Coronet, Div. of Esquire, Inc. 65 E. South Water St., Chicago, IL 60601
DEGR	Walter de Gruyter, Inc. 200 Sawmill River Rd., Hawthorne, N.Y. 10532
DOCA	Document Associates, Inc. 573 Church Street, Toronto, Canada
EAL	Ealing Film Loops 2225 Massachusetts Ave., Cambridge, MA 02140

EBEC	Encyclopedia Britannica Educational Corp. 425 N. Michigan Ave., Chicago, IL 60611
EDC	Educational Development Center 39 Chapel St., Newton, MA 02160
FA	Film Associates of California 11559 Santa Monica Blvd., Los Angeles, CA 90025
FHS	Films for the Humanities and Sciences P. O. Box 2053, Princeton, NJ 08543
HFC	Handel Film Corporation 8730 Sunset Blvd., Los Angeles, CA 90069
HRW	Holt, Rinehart and Winston 383 Madison Ave., New York, NY 10017
IFB	International Film Bureau 332 South Michigan Ave., Chicago, IL 60604
INUAVC	Teaching Film Custodians (Order through Film Distribution Center, University of Indiana, Bloomington, IN 47405)
JF	Journal Films 930 Piner Ave., Evanston, IL 60202
KALMIA	Kalmia Company Dept. P-1, Concord, MA 01742
MCGH	Mcgraw-Hill Textfilms 330 W. 42nd St., New York, NY 10018
MIS	Moody Institute of Science 12000 E. Washington Blvd., Whittier, CA 90608
MLA	Modern Learning Aids P.O. Box 312, Rochester, NY 14601
NASA	Order from NAVC (see next entry)
NAVC	National Audio-Visual Center General Service Administration Reference Station, Washington, DC 20409
NCSU	North Carolina State University Raleigh, NC 27650

NTSU	North Texas State University, Department of Physics Denton, TX 76203
OHSU	Ohio State University 159 W. 19th Ave., Columbus, OH 43210
PERED	Perennial Education, Inc. 447 Roger Williams, Highland Park, IL 60035
PSU	Applied Research Laboratory Pennsylvania State University P.O. Box 30, State College, PA 16801
PURDUE	Purdue University Audio-Visual Center Rm. 54 Stew, Lafayette, IN 47097
PYRAMID	Pyramid Film Productions P.O. Box 1048, Santa Monica, CA 90406
RPI	Rensselear Polytechnic Institute Troy, NY 12181
SMITH	Steve Smith Associates 2341 Grant St., Berkely, CA 94703
STERLED	Sterling Educational Films, Inc. 241 E. 34th St., New York, NY 10016
TIME	Time-Life Films Multimedia Div. 100 Eisenhower Dr., Paramus, NJ 07652
UCMC	University of California Extension Media Center 2223 Fulton St., Berkely, CA 94720
UEVA	University Education and Visual Arts Div. of Universal City Studios, Inc. 100 Universal City Plaza, Universal City, CA 91608
UIAVC	University of Iowa Audio-Visual Center Media Library C-5 East Hall, Iowa City, IA 52242
USAEC	United States Atomic Energy Commission Division of Public Information Audio-Visual Branch, Washington, DC 20545
VIKAS	Vikas Productions, Inc. P. O. Box 6088 Bozeman, MT 59771

COMPUTERS

Computers are now making significant contributions to the teaching of physics. They are used effectively in lectures to provide animated illustrations, with parameters varied by the lecturer; they also provide tutorials and drills which students can work through outside of class. The Physics Courseware Evaluation Project at the North Carolina State University (NCSU) maintains a current catalog of both commercial and public domain software; this was last published in *Computers in Physics* January/February 1993. This project reports recent developments in a quarterly newsletter, *Physics Courseware Communicator*, established in August 1993. Subscriptions ($15 per year) are available from:

> Physics Courseware Evaluation Project
> Department of Physics
> North Carolina State University
> Raleigh, NC 27695-8202

An (October 1991) conference titled Computational Physics in the Undergraduate Curriculum was held at Davidson College. For information on obtaining the conference proceedings write to Dr. Wolfgang, Davidson College, Davidson, NC 28036.

Probably the best single source for information on what is available in this rapidly evolving technology is a service operated by AIP with the joint sponsorship of AAPT and APS. For information on this service write:

> Physics Academic Software Library
> North Carolina State University
> P. O. Box 8202
> Raleigh, N.C. 27690-0739

This instructor's resource manual for Cutnell/Johnson lists for various chapters of the text four types of computer exercises suitable for use by students in a College Physics course. Most **spreadsheet** references are on the **Teaching Aids** page of the appropriate chapter. The other three categories (**computer programs, computer projects, and interactive videodisk**) are listed under **Computer Resources** for each chapter. Each entry includes: name (or title), publisher (or supplier), computer, and a brief description. In addition there are several packages that cover large portions of the typical course called College Physics. Four widely available packages are:

INTERACTIVE PHYSICS (KNowledge Revolution). This simulation program, which uses a minimum of mathematics, permits simulation of almost any motion experiment the student (or instructor) can think of. The package contains a wide variety of laboratory activities (using the Macintosh Plus computer) in mechanics, student worksheets, and notes for the instructor.

PHYSICS I AND PHYSICS II SERIES (Control Data Company). Excellent tutorials in problem solving for use with the IBM PC. Sixteen modules cover topics in mechanics; twelve modules are devoted to electrostatics, magnetostatics, and Faraday's law.

PHYSICS I and PHYSICS II (Microphysics Programs). Each set contains an interactive tutorial diskette, a problem generating diskette, and an answer/grading diskette. Different versions are available for IBM PC, Apple II, TRS-80 (models III and IV), Commodore 64/128, and most IBM compatibles.

PHYSICS SIMULATIONS (Kinko's). Many demonstrations from all areas of introductory physics. Individual programs are listed for appropriate chapters in the **Computer Resources** section. For the Apple Macintosh.

SENSEI PHYSICS (Broderbund Software). Tutorials using animated graphics for many areas of introductory physics. Over 300 practice problems. For Macintosh computers.

You might consider setting aside a room or portion of a lab, equip it with several computers, and make tutorial, drill, and simulation programs available to students. If you have sufficient hardware (and software), you might base some assignments on computer materials. Computers might also be used by students to perform calculations. Properly selected problems can add greatly to the students' understanding of physics. Problems involving the investigation of some physical system of interest might be assigned as individual projects or might be carried out in the laboratory.

Some institutions are making extensive use of coordinated computer packages in their introductory physics courses. A well known example is CUPLE (Comprehensive Unified Physics Learning Environment) developed at the University of Maryland by Dr. Edward F. Redish and Dr. Jack M. Wilson (now at Rensselaer Polytechnic Institute). CUPLE uses computer programs, interactive video discs, and a variety of sensors to collect data.

Commercial spreadsheet programs, of the type used by business, can facilitate problem solving. For a detailed account of how they are used and a collection of informative problems, see *Wondering About Physics ... Using Spreadsheets to Find Out* by D.I. Dykstra and R.G. Fuller (John Wiley & Sons, 1988). Selections from this collection are listed in this instructor's resource manual under **Spreadsheets** on the **Teaching Aids** page for each chapter. Another useful source for ideas on using spreadsheets is *Spreadsheet Physics*, Charles Misner and Patrick Cooney, Addison-Wesley (1991). Using Lotus 1-2-3 spreadsheets, this book is directed primarily at calculus-level courses, but some of the material is suitable for algebra-based physics courses. *Dynamic Models in Physics* by F. Potter and C. W. Peck, N. Simpson & Company (1989) is also a useful reference for solving physics problems using spreadsheets. Helpful suggestions on using spreadsheets are given in *The Physics Teacher 31* , 546 (1993).

Commercial problem solving programs such as *Eureka: The Solver* (Borland International) and *TK Solver!* (Universal Technical Systems Inc.) can easily be used by students to solve problems and graph results. In many cases, data generated by spreadsheets can also be imported to graph drawing programs. All these programs allow students to set up a problem generically, then view solutions for various values of input parameters. For example, the range or maximum height of a projectile can be found as a function of initial speed or firing angle, even when air resistance is taken into account.

KEY TO COMPUTER RESOURCES

Borland International (Eureka!)
4585 Scotts Valley Drive, Scotts Valley, CA 95066

Broderbund Software
P.O. Box 12947, San Rafael, CA 94913

Cambridge Development Laboratory
1696 Massachusetts Avenue, Cambridge, MA 02138

Conduit, The University of Iowa, Oakdale Campus
Iowa City, IA 52242

Control Data Corporation
3601 West 77th Street, Bloomington, MN 55435

Cross Educational Software
P.O. Box 1536, Ruston, LA 71270

Mark Davids
21825 O'Conner, St. Clair Shores, MI 48080

Educational Materials and Equipment Company
P.O. Box 17
Pelham, NY 10803

EduTech
634 Commonwealth Avenue, Newton Center, MA 02159

Focus Media, Inc.
839 Stewart Avenue, Garden City, NY 11530

R.H. Good, Physics Department
California State University at Hayward, CA 94542

High Technology Software Products
P.O. Box 60406, 1611 NW 23rd Street, Oklahoma City, OK 73146

HRM Software
175 Tompkins Avenue, Pleasantville, NY 10570-9973

ITE Software
6220 S. Orange Blossom Trail, Suite 316, Orlando, FL 32809

J&S Software
140 Reed Avenue, Port Washington, NY 11050

Kinko's Service Corporation
4141 State Street, Santa Barbara, CA 93110

Knowledge Revolution
15 Brush Place, San Francisco, CA 94103

Merlan Scientific Ltd.
247 Armstrong Ave, Georgetown, Ontario L7G 4X6, Canada

Microphysics Programs
12 Bridal Way, Sparta, NJ 07871

Norwalk High School, Science Department
County Street, Norwalk, CT 06851

Programs for Learning, Inc.
P.O. Box 954, New Milford, CT 06776

6502 Program Exchange
2920 Moana, Reno, NV 89509

Sunburst Communications
39 Washington Ave, Pleasantville, NY 10570

Vernier Software
2920 S.W. 89th Street, Portland, OR 97225

John Wiley & Sons, Inc., College Division
605 Third Avenue, New York, NY 10158-6088

SUGGESTED COURSES AND SAMPLE SCHEDULES

Like almost all books written for the college physics course that assumes a knowledge of algebra and some trigonometry, *Physics* by **John D. Cutnell and Kenneth W. Johnson** contains more material than can be covered in detail in a one-year course. We have in mind the typical course that carries 8 semester hours (or 12 quarter hours) credit. Most courses have a laboratory that students take concurrently. The book can also be used with a course that does not have a laboratory. In this case, however, the amount of material that can be covered in class will be somewhat less because, presumably, the laboratory experience will help students learn some of the material outside class.

We have prepared suggested schedules for a two-semester course and for a three-quarter course. We assumed that the class meets for three hours (50 minute hours) of lecture per week for 14 weeks each semester and for two-thirds of this (i.e., for about 10 weeks each quarter) if on the quarter system. Thus the schedules are based on 42 class meetings per semester (or 28 class meetings per quarter). Please note that we assumed that the course does not have a recitation meeting. We assumed that the first class of each term is devoted to orientation and the last class to review. We allowed for three tests during each semester and two during each quarter. This leaves 37 lectures per semester in which to cover the material. For the quarter system, we felt that a full orientation day would not be needed each quarter and that the review session at the end of the quarter would be somewhat less than a full class period. Thus we assumed 25 lectures available per quarter for covering the material in the book. We did not allow class time for a final examination because this is usually built into the college calendar.

Among colleges on the semester system, there is nearly complete uniformity for the sequence in which topics are considered, viz., mechanics, heat, and sound the first semester and electricity, optics, and modern physics the second semester. There is considerably more variation in the sequence of covering topics among institutions using the quarter system. Textbooks and professors typically allocate more time for mechanics (about 30%) than for any other topic, with electricity and magnetism being the second largest block (20% to 25%). Thus mechanics fits nicely as the sole topic for the first quarter of a three-quarter academic year, but it is not possible to devote an entire quarter to electricity and magnetism. The typical time allocations for the other topics (heat, sound, optics, and modern physics) are such that there are essentially two choices for sequencing the topics: (1) follow the semester sequence and split electricity between the second and third quarters, or (2) depart from the semester sequence and cover all of electricity (and some other material) during a single quarter. We have prepared a suggested sequence for each of these quarter system options.

The large number of topics in the textbook allow the instructor flexibility in choosing material pertinent to the needs of his/her class. The text can be adapted to serve the needs of a variety of student majors. The material that will be emphasized in a particular course depends on the approach used by the instructor. Thus the suggested schedules we have prepared include all chapters of the book. We did assume that the sections marked by an asterisk (*) in the book would not be covered in class, at least not in detail. The time allocated to each chapter is usually not sufficient to permit detailed coverage of all material in that chapter. Thus instructors will need to choose which sections will be omitted or covered only cursorily. It is possible, of course, to omit entire chapters if the emphasis of the course is on detailed coverage of a limited number of topics. We felt, however, that the suggested schedules should include material from each chapter because many students (e.g., premedical students) often need a broad coverage to prepare for MCAT or similar professional type examinations. The suggested schedules are sufficiently flexible and complete that they should serve as a basis on which each instructor can construct a more detailed schedule to serve the needs of his/her students.

SUGGESTED SCHEDULE: TWO-SEMESTER COURSE					
First Semester			**Second Semester**		
Text Chapter	Number of Lectures	Cumulative Lectures	Text Chapter	Number of Lectures	Cumulative Lectures
1	2.0	2.0	18	2.8	2.8
2	2.3	4.3	19	2.6	5.4
3	1.7	6.0	20	4.0	9.4
4	3.4	9.4	21	3.5	12.9
5	1.5	10.9	22	3.5	16.4
6	2.2	13.1	23	2.3	18.7
7	1.6	14.7			
8	1.3	16.0	24	1.8	20.5
9	2.5	18.5	25	1.8	22.3
10	2.2	20.7	26	4.2	26.5
11	3.0	23.7	27	2.8	29.3
12	2.8	26.5	28	1.5	30.8
13	1.4	27.9	29	1.2	32.0
14	1.5	29.4	30	2.0	34.0
15	3.1	32.5	31	1.5	35.5
			32	1.5	37.0
16	2.7	35.2			
17	1.8	37.0			

SUGGESTED SCHEDULE: THREE-QUARTER COURSE
(WITHOUT SPLITTING ANY MAIN SECTION)

First Quarter			Second Quarter		
Text Chapter	Number of Lectures	Cumulative Lectures	Text Chapter	Number of Lectures	Cumulative Lectures
1	2.1	2.1	12	2.9	2.9
2	2.4	4.5	13	1.5	4.4
3	1.8	6.3	14	1.6	6.0
4	3.6	9.9	15	3.2	9.2
5	1.6	11.5			
6	2.3	13.8	16	2.9	12.1
7	1.7	15.5	17	1.9	14.0
8	1.4	16.9			
9	2.6	19.5	24	1.9	15.9
10	2.3	21.8	25	1.9	17.8
11	3.2	25.0	26	4.3	22.1
			27	2.9	25.0

Third Quarter		
Text Chapter	Number of Lectures	Cumulative Lectures
18	2.7	2.7
19	2.5	5.2
20	3.8	9.0
21	3.3	12.3
22	3.3	15.6
23	2.2	17.8
28	1.4	19.2
29	1.1	20.3
30	1.9	22.2
31	1.4	23.6
32	1.4	25.0

SUGGESTED SCHEDULE: THREE-QUARTER COURSE
(WITH ELECTRICITY SPLIT BETWEEN QUARTERS)

First Quarter			Second Quarter		
Text Chapter	Number of Lectures	Cumulative Lectures	Text Chapter	Number of Lectures	Cumulative Lectures
1	2.1	2.1	12	3.0	3.0
2	2.4	4.5	13	1.7	4.7
3	1.8	6.3	14	1.7	6.4
4	3.6	9.9	15	3.4	9.8
5	1.6	11.5			
6	2.3	13.8	16	2.9	12.7
7	1.7	15.5	17	2.1	14.8
8	1.4	16.9			
9	2.6	19.5	18	3.1	17.9
10	2.3	21.8	19	2.8	20.7
11	3.2	25.0	20	4.3	25.0

Third Quarter		
Text Chapter	Number of Lectures	Cumulative Lectures
21	3.2	3.2
22	3.2	6.4
23	2.1	8.5
24	1.6	10.1
25	1.6	11.7
26	3.8	15.5
27	2.8	18.3
28	1.3	19.6
29	1.0	20.6
30	1.8	22.4
31	1.3	23.7
32	1.3	25.0

IDEAS FOR THE FIRST TIME LECTURER

ABSTRACT

Aspiring and aging professor of physics, A.B. in English (Phi Beta Kappa), Ph.D. in Physics (Sigma Xi), 36 years experience in quality institutions (College of William and Mary, Oak Ridge National Laboratory, and Old Dominion University), seeks opportunity to converse with inspiring young assistant professors of physics for the purpose of exploring the art of teaching our favorite subject to today's students.

HOW I GOT HERE

A few months ago, in a moment of either great weakness or deceptive anticipation, I agreed to write a few pages of comments that might be helpful to some newly minted, academically certified, moderately ambitious assistant professor of physics. Ever since that ill-fated moment, I've been racking my brain in an effort to extract some nuggets of wisdom to share with the first time lecturer. But the ideas that sounded so profound and brilliant when discussed informally with colleagues over the years seemed to have lost their luster when I tried to put them in writing. Of course, I shouldn't really be surprised by this; it's certainly not the first time I've been surprised as a teacher. This leads me to suggest that the first time lecturer would do well to get used to surprises. Let me mention a few that I, and most of the physics professors I know, have encountered along the way.

THREE SURPRISES I'VE ENCOUNTERED

My first full-time college appointment was in the fall of 1958. This was the first academic year following the launching of Sputnik some eleven months earlier. The fairly prestigious college that took a chance on me had very good students and, because of the space race with its emphasis on science, a goodly number of these students enrolled in physics. They were bright; I was a novice. The interaction of the bright and eager students with the inexperienced but determined teacher led the latter to his first surprise which, in reality, is a closely related pair of surprises.

THE FIRST SURPRISE: I remember being surprised at how quickly the students learned at first, at how rapidly they absorbed (and, I thought, even mastered) the material as I led them through translational kinematics and dynamics. I distinctly remember a feeling of trepidation that at this rate of learning these students' knowledge of physics would soon surpass mine, at which time I wouldn't even be able to keep a chapter ahead of them. And then about midsemester I noticed that most of them no longer learned the material at first glance; indeed some even had to struggle almost as much as I had some years previously in a similar university physics course. I had to go more slowly, to discuss principles from several perspectives, to give more examples than previously. Much to my surprise, the class that initially had learned so effortlessly now labored to understand linear momentum and kinetic energy. What joy I felt in joining faculty colleagues, occasionally even senior ones, in bemoaning the sad state of today's students as we longed for scholars who were as eager and talented as we had been. But in more reflective moments I began to realize that the students were still bright--it was just that they had reached a learning plateau with the result that a considerable incubation period was needed to absorb new concepts and, especially, to correlate these with principles previously ingested. Gradually I began to understand that a tightly-structured, sequential discipline such as physics--particularly Newtonian mechanics--requires a rather extensive incubation period. It's so easy (not to mention convenient) for seasoned physicists and accomplished teachers to forget the inordinate amount of time we spent (we thought it was wasted) in making false starts, going down blind alleys, and pursuing wayward detours before we managed to integrate different aspects of physics into a meaningful pattern that enabled us to appreciate, or even to see, the forest rather than experience bewilderment as we stared at the multiplicity of trees. While I still try to adhere to high standards for student performance, I try to be more patient if they don't immediately comprehend all of the subtleties.

THE SECOND SURPRISE: Another surprise is how little interest most of the students in my introductory courses have in physics. Why don't they share my enthusiasm for the topic under discussion? Why do they apparently spend as little time on physics as they can get away with? I asked them to look at some questions and problems at the end of the kinematics chapter--and then when I tried to hold a discussion in class, it was soon evident that most of them didn't get around to the assignment. Well, to be honest, as a student I myself very seldom got around to college assignments that were not to be turned in. It wasn't that I was uninterested or totally lazy. It's just that I was so busy doing homework for those courses in which assignments were collected that I had no time left for optional academic pursuits. It's amazing how little time students (and indeed most of us) have for those activities that are optional and how much time we can find for activities that are required. As one of my Navy friends put it, *"You get what you inspect, not what you expect."* So I insist that my students hand in a homework assignment once a week. Subsequently I'll discuss homework assignments and grading in more detail.

THE THIRD SURPRISE: This last surprise pertains not to students--but to me. When I first became a faculty member, I was surprised at how much time teaching a physics course took. As a graduate student I had done some teaching that, although demanding, had not required nearly as much time as when I became a faculty member. Gradually I realized that there is a difference between being an assistant who serves a limited role in a course and being a faculty member who assumes full responsibility for the viability of the entire course--the lecture, the laboratory, the recitation, the tests, and perhaps most important, the students. I was also surprised that so little time was available for preparing for class--there always seemed to be committees, visitors, students, reports required by the administration, a proposal to write, a research project to help with, etc. Somehow one has to learn to budget one's time and to invest it wisely--not that I've been very effective at this.

So much for three surprises--three among many. Let me now discuss the rationale for the lecture system; after this I will make some suggestions regarding skills and techniques that may be helpful in lecturing.

IS THE LECTURE SYSTEM HERE TO STAY?

Yes, it is. At least I think it is. You know why? Well, as I tell my students, a lecture has been aptly defined as an ingenious device by which information in the instructor's notes is transferred to the student's notes without passing through the heads of either. The student is willing to pay tuition (i.e., money) for the privilege and pleasure of participating in this system and the professoriate gets paid, some rather handsomely, for services rendered. Now who is going to agitate to abolish such an arrangement? Viewed from another perspective, the lecture has been around a long time and doubtless has survived onslaughts from administrators who want to be more cost efficient and from various and sundry other constituencies. But the system has survived, even thrived. Surely such a long-lived system must be serving some societal, and perhaps even educational, purpose. Of course, I readily admit that the lecture is a very expensive and inefficient method of transmitting information. Once, as a naive idealist, I informed my class that the lecture really should have been abolished shortly after the invention of the printing press--and that henceforth I would expect them to become conversant with the factual material in the textbook on their own and that time in class would be used to answer any questions they might have, to explain any ambiguities in the text, and most importantly to explore through mutual discussion the subtleties and implications of the facts--with me serving as a resource person, moderator, and mentor (like Socrates, you know). This novelty lasted almost a couple of days, whereupon we settled again into the tried and proven (or at least accepted) lecture system. The imminent departure of the lecture has been repeatedly forecast since at least the mid-1700's, as witness Boswell's quoting [1] Dr. Samuel Johnson as saying:

> *"Lectures were once useful; but now, when all can read,*
> *and books are so numerous, lectures are unnecessary. If*
> *your attention fails, and you miss part of the lecture, it is*
> *lost; you cannot go back as you do upon a book."*

(Have I not read virtually these same words within the last year except that the word **books** was replaced by **computers**?) Despite such dire prognostications, statements regarding the death of the lecture system--like statements pertaining to the demise of Mark Twain--have been greatly exaggerated. I will return later to the lecture system and speak positively about some of its strengths. I merely wanted in this present section to establish some basis to support the view that the lecture system is here to stay and that, therefore, it is worthwhile for the beginning physics teacher to acquire some skills and techniques that experienced lecturers have found useful. We turn now to this task.

THE *SINE QUA NON* FOR GOOD LECTURERS

Before considering specific skills and strategies that successful physics lecturers have found useful, I want to make some general comments regarding the overall approach to being a good teacher of introductory physics. Let me first set forth what I perceive to be our ultimate objective as teachers. I can do no better than to cite [2] the "Report of Conferences on the Improvement of College Teaching" and to say that I agree with the distinguished physics professors (Francis Bitter, Francis L. Friedman, Walter C. Michels, Francis W. Sears, Frank Verbrugge, and Jerrold R. Zacharias) who prepared the report in 1960. They state:

> *"The overall aim of college physics teaching is the same*
> *as that of all higher education: to help students think and*
> *act in ways appropriate to the modern world."*

Note that our goal is to "*help students think and act.*" Every word here is significant. We are to **help.** We can no more do the thinking and acting for the student than we can digest his/her food. We cannot grow, we cannot study, we cannot learn for the student. In fact, we cannot do anything for a person that a person **must** do for himself; we can only help. But note that we physicists do not have to do all of the helping. While I contend that, even among the sciences, physics has something unique to contribute, let us be aware that other professors, other disciplines, other college experiences will do part of the helping. Of the four key words in the phrase quoted above, two (**think** and **act**) will be addressed in a subsequent section. The fourth key word, **students**, has a central role in the following section in which I discuss four facets of knowledge that are essential (i.e., *sine qua non*) for the first time lecturer, the last time lecturer, and all other lecturers anywhere in between on the road from beginning to retiring.

FOUR THINGS YOU MUST KNOW

First, and by far the most important, **KNOW YOUR SUBJECT**. There is no way at all that we can teach college physics so as to "*help students think and act ... in ways appropriate to the modern world*" if we do not know our discipline, our physics. I do not propose to say anything further on this topic because I trust that the college that appointed this newly minted, first time lecturer assured itself that he/she met this primary qualification. I would note, however, that knowing a subject and teaching the subject are different. As I prepare for my classes, I try not only to refresh my knowledge of the physics to be covered but also to think back to long ago days when I was learning this part of physics. I find it helpful to recall the difficulties I had in understanding these particular concepts. In short, I try to become a beginner again so that I can anticipate the difficulties my students will encounter as they try to follow the concepts I'm trying to help them learn. This brings me to the second essential thing a first time lecturer needs to know.

Second, **KNOW YOUR STUDENTS**. I went into teaching physics because I wanted to teach physics. But it didn't take very long to realize that while it doubtless would be nice to **teach physics**, that option was not available to me. Why not? Well, simply because my assignment was to **teach physics to students**--and that was much more difficult but also ultimately much more rewarding. We need to know something about how students learn (i.e., the cognitive process), about the emotional and intellectual development of young persons just entering college, about the tensions they experience in daily living, about how to motivate them, and about the demands that disciplines other than physics place on them. Rather than expounding at length on our need to be conversant with matters of this type, I will forthwith summon an expert witness who will establish beyond reasonable doubt that we need to know our students. The witness is Robert A. Millikan, recipient in 1940 of the Oersted Medal awarded by the American Association of Physics teachers for "notable contributions to the teaching of physics." Here [3] is his testimony:

> "*The most important job of the teacher is to know his students, every one of them, so that he will make as few mistakes as possible in rating their qualities and their capacities justly and accurately in order that he may steer them wisely. Talking entertainingly to a hundred or two hundred students is a wholly subordinate and trivial requirement of a good teacher. The great, indispensable requisite is conscientiousness in watching carefully and discriminatingly the way his students solve problems, the way they do their laboratory work, the way they answer questions, the way they pose questions of their own. This job cannot be delegated to anyone else without abdicating the main job of the teacher.*"

Knowing your students also implies knowing your class as an entity. This means knowing their capacity, their intellectual potential, their present knowledge of the subject. Knowing these abilities will help you to avoid both dwelling overly long on the obvious (and thereby boring most of the class) and spending too much time on the incomprehensible (and thereby losing almost everyone).

Knowing the persons on one side of the lecture desk will not result in effective teaching unless you also know the human on the opposite of the desk. Thus the third essential component is: **KNOW YOURSELF**. As has already been mentioned, without a doubt you know your subject. It is almost equally certain that you know yourself fairly well. You rose to the challenge of earning a Ph.D. in physics and, perhaps after serving a postdoctoral, you found a college position. Thus you almost certainly are intelligent, resourceful, and persistent; these will stand you in good stead as you begin teaching full time. While pursuing your doctorate, you probably served a year or two as a graduate teaching assistant and thereby acquired experience in supervising a laboratory, teaching a recitation section, grading homework, and perhaps even lecturing to introductory classes once in a while. Now that you are among the professoriate, you will need to know yourself even better. Is college teaching really your cup of tea? How will you apportion your time among the competing demands of research, teaching, committee work, and service to the college, to professional organizations, and to the community in which you live? Be assured that a nearby school will invite you to speak to their science club and/or to judge a science fair. All of these involvements take time and any one of them could consume almost all of your time (as well as your energy and creative drive) if you let it. Allocation of your time to various endeavors is something you must decide. Talk to faculty colleagues--young ones like yourself, those somewhat older who have recently achieved tenure, and the more senior ones who've survived in *la academe*. Determine what the reward structure at your institution is--and meet the requirements of that structure or seek your fortune elsewhere.

Each new assistant professor has different talents to offer and each has different priorities. But I strongly urge everyone to **stay involved in research and to be an effective teacher**. I would try **to achieve excellence either in research or in teaching** and to make at least a modest contribution in the other. I tend toward the view that the major thrust of your work during the first few years should be toward getting a research program established on campus. If you are at an institution that offers graduate degrees in physics, you almost certainly will need to be active in research to have any chance of getting tenure. Effective teaching is essential also--but good teaching alone usually will not lead to tenure. There are, of course, many different types of institutions, and what holds at a university may not have the same priority at a liberal arts college or a community college. In any event, even if one has a situation in which involvement in physics research is nearly impossible, all of us should be engaged in some type of scholarly activity beyond the classroom. The point of this section is that you need to know your abilities, your interests, your goals, and your own limitations--and allocate your time and effort accordingly, realizing that you cannot be all things to all students, all committees, all research involvements. You must learn to focus your efforts, or you will be perceived as reasonably effective in many areas but with no distinctive excellence in any one area--in other words, jack of all trades and master of none. And this, for an untenured assistant professor, usually leads to a dead end. A dead end leads nowhere--but the end of this paragraph leads to the fourth thing you must know.

KNOW YOUR PEDAGOGY. At least know enough about pedagogy to be aware of simple skills and techniques that have helped physics professors (and others too) to become competent in the craft of teaching. In this context we are interested in applied pedagogy, in those tricks of the trade that are directly and immediately useful to the first time lecturer--so instead of becoming philosophical in discussing this fourth essential, I will terminate this present section and get down to brass tacks in the next.

HOW TO LECTURE: SKILLS AND TECHNIQUES

How much of your lecture should be devoted to going over material covered in the text? How closely should you follow the text? Should you use lecture notes? What kind? Should you rehearse your lecture beforehand? Is it best to use a microphone in lecturing to large classes? How should one handle students who want to talk in class? Is it worthwhile to assign homework? How much homework? Is grading homework and tests very time consuming? These "nuts and bolts" items will be addressed in this section. Let me note that the guideline established for me by the John Wiley Physics Editor is that this section should be "what an experienced/successful College Physics instructor would relate to a colleague teaching the course for the first time." I make no claim to being very successful, but I cannot deny that I've been around a long time and hence am experienced. Should a first time lecturer seek my counsel, I seriously doubt that I would give him/her a learned and tightly woven lecture. On the contrary, I probably would ramble a great deal and take excursions along side roads as the two of us talked about the "methods and materials" of teaching. This is the approach I'll use here--except that I'll record only my part of the dialogue.

AN INFORMAL CHAT WITH A FIRST TIME LECTURER

I'll tell you about the things that work well for me. Others have found that a different style works best for them. You'll want to develop your own style--if you don't, you'll never enjoy teaching. I'm flattered that you came to me first to discuss teaching, but please be sure to talk with several other faculty members, especially to some of the younger, but still experienced, ones. You were asking about the **syllabus**. I myself use a one-page syllabus and tend to doubt the effectiveness of a syllabus of more than four or five pages. I include the following:

Information about the course: the course number, the section number, the class meeting days and hours; information as appropriate on recitation (if any) and lab.

Information about myself: my name, room and phone numbers for my office, my office hours.

Materials for the course: I also indicate which items are required and which are optional. Typical materials are: textbook, lab manual, calculator, study guide, type of notebooks for lecture and for lab, ruler, graph paper, etc.

Information on testing and grading: I state the number of tests (I give three); some semesters I specify the dates for each test; other semesters I omit the dates and just state that tests will be announced at least one week in advance. I specify the relative weighting of each component (tests, exam, homework, lab, recitation) in determining the final grade in the course.

Information pertaining to homework: Format for submitting homework (kind of paper, how folded, etc); when assigned (I assign homework one week in advance of due date); due date; penalty for late homework; where to turn homework in (I use a hallway locker--I don't like the hassle of turning homework in in class and the confrontation that often ensues when a student turns his/hers in after class rather than at the beginning); state that I will respond (in class) to general inquiries regarding homework but not help students individually with homework; whether homework is pledged or not (I encourage my students to work together on homework and to get help from anyone other than me); when and where homework solutions will be posted or otherwise made available.

Classroom Management (Housekeeping): Are seats assigned? If so, how? (I let students choose where to sit in class; then I assign the seats accordingly. I assign different seats for tests.) Is roll taken? Is attendance required? Are make-up tests given? If so, on what basis? Can formula sheets be used on tests? Are some formulas given? How about constants?

In summary, I put on the syllabus the minimum essential information that I believe the student needs to know in order to participate meaningfully in the course. Other, perhaps most, teachers use a longer syllabus that might include course objectives, list of chapters (or topics) to be covered and on what date, reading assignments, homework assignments for the entire semester and due dates, hints on studying, problem solving, etc. My own experience is that students invariably fail to get excited about supposedly compelling statements of lofty objectives; students focus their concerns on what tests will be like and how the teacher grades. That is what I give then on the syllabus. Then I try to take care of the other (and more important) matters-- such as excitement, commitment, and insight--during the rest of the semester. No matter what approach you use in your syllabus, I would suggest: (1) following local guidelines and practices as to what should be put in the syllabus, (2) keeping the syllabus fairly short (two or three pages maximum), (3) making the syllabus functional rather than philosophical, (4) designing the syllabus to be useful to the student rather than as a massive document intended to impress some administrator, and (5) not wasting time and effort by having the department secretary copy into the syllabus the table of contents of the textbook.

AN ASIDE TO THE READER: In real time, the preceding discussion would have taken three or four minutes; I'd simply give the person copies of two or three syllabi used by me and make brief comments on them.

THE FIRST CLASS MEETING

You asked a moment ago if it's okay to include on the syllabus comments on matters such as: how I conduct the class, whether students can interrupt to ask questions, suggestions to students on studying, taking notes, and reading ahead. Certainly it's okay to include these items. In fact, it's okay to include anything you want to. My own approach is to discuss matters of this sort at the first class meeting rather than on the syllabus, but this is really a matter of taste or style. This first class meeting is very important; you know the old saying that first impressions are lasting. Let the class know what your approach to lecturing is. I tend to stick fairly close to the book in the ordering of topics. My lecture notes (such as they are) and the notes I write on the overhead projector (or board) in class are built around the text. The faculty have selected what they consider to be a good text, and the students have paid dearly for the book, so I use the book as the scaffolding around which to teach the course. I do give additional examples, especially ones that involve pertinent current news events, such as the major earthquake in California that was on the front page of the local newspaper the day I wrote these words. But back to the first day of class. I introduce myself, welcome them, hand out the syllabus--and then I go over the syllabus with them step by step. I let them ask questions. I try to come across as a real person. (Actually I don't try to; I want to and hope I do--but I don't try to, because then I won't.) I make additional comments on my lecture style and on the other items you asked about above. I tell them that this course will be demanding and that my expectations are high but reasonable and realistic. I let them know that I am available to help them outside class if they will take the initiative to come see me. And one other thing I try to do the first day; I try to cover some physics. Although it may be for only five minutes, I like to get the course started--and for them to realize that the course has started and that they also need to get started. So much for the syllabus and the first day of class. The ice has been broken; teacher and students have faced each other across the lecture table and both have survived. Now let's consider the next class; you'll have a full period to talk about physics then.

PROJECTORS AND CHALKBOARDS

Most physics teachers try to communicate with their students both orally and visually. That is, we talk (so students will hear the physics) and we write (so that they will see what we are talking about). Let's consider some useful guidelines on the effective use of seeing and hearing. In discussing the art of giving a lecture, George E. Uhlenbeck, co-discoverer of electron spin, recalls [4] the advice he and his fellow students received from their physics professor.

"I can still hear Ehrenfest exclaim in his typical mixture of German and Dutch when one of us students gave a talk: 'Please, start writing on the upper left-hand corner of the blackboard!; please, do not erase before people have a chance to see what you wrote; please, do not talk with your face to the blackboard,' etc. All perhaps rather trivial points but one has only to go to a meeting of the American Physical Society to see how often people sin against these rather simple rules."

This reminds me that you and I were chatting a couple of days ago about whether to use the chalkboard or the overhead projector. My own preference is the projector because I am facing the class while writing. Thus I can talk to them (not to the board); I can also see them and observe their reactions. Also, I can write in rather small letters, yet students in the rear of a fairly large lecture room can still see the diagrams and notes I make. Some teachers prefer the chalkboard. Paul G. Hewitt, of the City College of San Francisco, who is known far and wide as a superb teacher, uses the board. But whichever you use, be sure that what your writing is easily seen by students at the rear of the room. I also suggest that the diagrams you draw be clear, neat, and uncluttered. Just before you dropped by to chat, I was browsing through that new book we've adopted for our College Physics course--you know, the one by Cutnell and Johnson. One of the things I like about that book is that the drawings are elegantly simple and each figure concentrates on a single main idea. One picture is worth a thousand words--but only if the picture is focused.

One reason I prefer the overhead projector to the chalkboard is that most introductory level physics textbooks are now accompanied by transparencies of many of the figures in the text; Cutnell and Johnson's book has 300 of these. Another reason is that it is easy for me to make good drawings on the acetate. In addition, I can also prepare drawings beforehand and bring them to class. This is especially desirable when the figure needs to drawn carefully and to scale rather than just being a rough sketch. As you know, our department has a photocopying machine that will make transparencies and will enlarge and reduce the size. This makes it fairly easy to make a transparency of any figure in the text and indeed from other books and journals. Lastly, I find that I can use different colors easily and effectively with the projector. You've probably heard other faculty members here remark that I'm not one to use a fancy, multicolored, precisely drawn transparency when a simple sketch is just as effective if not more so. Please let me caution you about using different colors to excess. Use colors to highlight the central ideas and to give some variety, but indiscriminate use of color to dazzle the student or just to make a cute drawing seems to me to be counterproductive.

I like the quote above in which Professor Ehrenfest urged that speakers "...*not erase before people have a chance to see what you wrote.*" I remember that in college we used to kid about old Professor X who wrote on the board with his right hand and immediately removed the writing with an eraser held in his left hand so that at any given instant the board contained only about three feet of writing--and Professor X stood directly in front of that. This is one of the difficulties with both the board and the projector--it's so easy to stand in front of the writing. Many instructors find it helpful to pause every few minutes, to step aside from the board or projector, and to wait for students to catch up. While at first the silence seems awkward, the change of pace may recapture the attention of some students who have been daydreaming about...about...well, let's just say they were daydreaming about something other than physics. This business of the mind wandering away from the subject being discussed leads me to make a few comments regarding the **attention span**.

THE ATTENTION SPAN

When my children were small, they enjoyed watching the Saturday morning cartoons on television. You've probably watched them yourself. Did you ever notice how short a given segment of a TV program (cartoon or otherwise) is before they switch to something different (and not necessarily just to another commercial). Take a look sometimes at some of the popular and highly rated children's educational programs such as Sesame Street or Newton's Apple. It often seems that they hardly get into a scene before they switch to another topic. Yet it's rather widely agreed that these programs are effective. Of course, the reason behind this frequent switching from one topic to another is the fact that children can concentrate on one idea for only a short time; after that the mind wanders. In other words, children have an **attention span** of a few minutes. But so do college students, at least the ones who are in my classes. I'm amazed by the scheduling of some college classes. For example, I know of a graduate level course (not in my department) that is scheduled from 6:00 p.m. to 9:45 p.m. with only one 10 minute break included. People put in a full day at work, grab a bite to eat, fight rush hour traffic to get to the university, and sit for four hours with only a 10 minute break! Whoever scheduled this may be able to count the minutes of class time needed to qualify for three semester hours credit, but I don't think they are aware that the mind can absorb no more than the seat can endure. For a graphic demonstration of the attention span, may I suggest that you attend a physics seminar, preferably one held just after lunch. Even though it's a topic in which you are interested, and even though the speaker is pretty good, notice how quickly the mind wanders and you feel inclined to doze off. This is especially true if, like the students in most college physics classes, you aren't able to follow the chain of development being presented.

It behooves all of us, whether first time lecturer or seasoned veteran, to be aware of the attention span and to have frequent changes of pace in our presentations. Some possibilities are: covering a concept and then presenting an example or two (going from the abstract to the concrete); taking a few minutes of class time and letting the students become actively involved by working an example themselves; using variety in our speaking pattern--varying the cadence a bit (e.g., using a slow cadence when we talk about a slowly moving train); varying the loudness with which we speak (talk in a whisper when you're explaining low decibel sounds); interspersing demonstrations throughout the class period; using a short film loop to vary the pace; providing the class with frequent breathing spaces (I've already mentioned stepping aside from the projector and waiting a minute or so for students to catch up); using gestures and a variety thereof; doing a bit of acting (e.g., if you're discussing translational, rotational, and vibrational degrees of freedom of molecules, pretend you're a water molecule with your head as **O** and your fists as **H's** and ham it up a bit. 'Tis silly, I know, but the students will perk up; (years later students will remember their half-witted professor, and they'll recall at least a little bit of physics along with the acting); providing the opportunity for questions or perhaps for comments; giving a pop quiz (guaranteed to get their attention); looking at different sections of the audience; trying to establish eye contact; pausing abruptly and waiting patiently while two students stop whispering to each other; using a bit of humor once in a while; making reference to current events or to persons in the news (I'm currently on a "Read my lips" kick--but one has to be very careful with matters bordering on politics or religion--also on sex). I could go on and on--like most professors, I'm very likely to keep going on and on--but I believe you get the idea. The important thing is to develop your own style; talk to others to get ideas but adapt them to your own talents and needs.

ORGANIZATION OF THE LECTURE

It may be helpful to talk a bit about organization of the lecture. Should one have detailed lecture notes? Should the lecture be tightly woven and somewhat formal? Should you repeat the key parts of the lecture so that those who didn't understand it the first time will have a chance to catch up? There are many approaches to organizing and presenting a lecture. One of the best I know is reputed to have come from a man who, though he had little formal education, had acquired a local reputation as an effective speaker. He explained his approach in simple terms:

"First I tell 'em what I'm gonna tell 'em.
Then I tell 'em.
Then I tell 'em what I told 'em."

From my experience in the classroom, I would add:

"Then if you're lucky,
Half of the time,
Half of the class will remember
Half of what you said...if you tell 'em again."

Often in our teaching we rush directly into a concept without giving the student a preliminary view of where we are headed and why. One of the things I noticed about Cutnell and Johnson is that they briefly explain the purpose of an upcoming example to help the student see the development in perspective. But we don't want to spend the whole class period telling the student what we are going to do. Better to give a brief overview and then proceed with the development. In doing so, it is important to speak to the student in terms that are meaningful to him/her. Just this morning an article in the local newspaper called attention to this in connection with a story in a basic reader being used by students at an inner city school. One of the teachers noted that the story was *"about a tractor factory in the midwest. Lots of our kids have never seen a tractor before and don't know how it works. They can't relate to the story."* When I was a youngster, all the children in my hometown knew that cream rose to the top of a bottle of unhomogenized milk; we had seen this many times. We understood when our science teacher used this experience in discussing density. Today's students have never seen cream rise to the top and generally do not know that cream is less dense than milk. In fact, most school students I've talked with infer that cream is denser than milk because cream pours more slowly (is more viscous). It's not that the students are ignorant or unobservant; it's just that they have different experiences. If the topic deals with projectile motion, students will perk up if the instructor illustrates time of flight by referring to the hang time of a football punt. In talking about momentum and impulse, it's helpful to call attention to a bat striking a baseball. We sometimes get so carried away with using esoteric examples as illustrations of physical laws that we overlook phenomena that students encounter every day. As Paul Hewitt remarked: [5]

> *"I feel uneasy about such things as students examining the photographs of bubble-chamber tracks when they don't understand bubbles in a carbonated drink or in boiling water."*

As for "telling 'em what you told 'em," it is advisable to review from time to time so that the class can view the development in hindsight. For example, when discussing rotational motion, first in terms of kinematics and then of dynamics, remind the students of the parallel path pursued in discussing translational motion. This helps them to assimilate the various concepts into a coherent pattern.

HOMEWORK, TESTS, AND GRADES

When I was discussing the syllabus with you, I indicated that I would make further comments regarding homework. I believe that it is essential to assign homework at least once a week and that it be collected and graded. Use as many techniques (such as homework) as you can to get students to participate actively in the course. Not only is experience the best teacher, **experience is the only teacher.** Arnold B. Arons, a physics professor who has played a leading role in research on the learning process, referred to: [6]

> *".. the widely prevalent illusion that students will master concepts, theories, and arts of thinking and reasoning through inculcation, i.e., by reading or by passive listening to sufficiently lucid expositions. This is demonstrably not the case. Activity must be induced within the intellect of each individual student."*

How much homework should one assign? There obviously are many different practices. My own approach is to assign three problems of moderate difficulty each week. An undergraduate student grades all problems, but not in the detail that is used in grading tests. (I grade the tests.) We grade the homework generously. Each problem is graded on a 10-point scale and deductions are made in half-point increments. I have found that students are much happier to have 0.5 of a point deducted on a 10-point scale than to lose 5 points on a 100-point scale. Although the proportions are the same in the two cases, student perception and reaction are different. This method saves me considerable time in discussing with individual students the grade on their homework. Rather than grading every assigned problem, some instructors count the number of problems solved and then grade one randomly selected problem in detail. I know of one large university in which homework problems are assigned with answers given in a multiple choice format, the primary reason being not to save time in grading but to avoid arguing with students about how much partial credit was given. Whatever grading scheme is used, I urge that homework be collected. In preparing hour tests for your class, ask your colleagues to give you samples from previous years. I try to return tests, especially the first test each semester, to the students as promptly as possible. Regarding a reasonable distribution of final grades in the course, I suggest that you talk with other faculty who have taught the same course and know what the pattern is at your institution.

DON'T TRY TO COVER THE WHOLE TEXTBOOK

One of the pitfalls of which all of us should be wary is that of rushing pell mell through the book whether students are with us or not. You may have heard the story about the professor who moved so fast through the book that when a student dropped his pencil, he got two chapters behind before he could pick it up. We are tempted to be comprehensive in our coverage, to give students an exposure to every topic discussed in the text. This is a treadmill that leads to frustration for both student and teacher. As was noted [7] in the 1960 report previously cited:

> *"We do well to realize that when we go too fast, or shoot over the heads of our students, we are likely to create frustration, bewilderment, and a loss of the self-confidence so essential to disciplined thinking."*

Textbooks tend to be encyclopedic in their coverage of topics. This rather comprehensive coverage allows flexibility and makes the book suitable for a broad range of courses that have somewhat different emphases. The authors and publishers of the book have little expectation that all of the book will be covered in any one course. Trying to do so leads us into the trap cited by Clifford E. Swartz in an editorial [8] titled *"Too much, too fast, too soon."* As an old saying puts it: *How much physics we cover is less important than how much physics we uncover.* As noted by

Philip Morrison in his classic lecture [9] *"Less may be more,"* covering fewer topics may result in teaching more physics. The decision on how much to cover is intimately related to the more fundamental question regarding what we want an introductory physics course to accomplish. Do we want to communicate just the factual content or do we also want our students to understand the process by which the facts came to be known? If we wish to explain as well as inform, we will have to limit coverage. As Arnold Arons put it: [10]

> *"There is, it seems to me, no alternative to slowing up, cutting off some of the desperate coverage, even if it is as painful as cutting off a finger or an arm, and giving the students a chance to focus some attention on the process in which knowledge and understanding of a new concept are acquired."*

In deciding on a suitable pace at which to cover the subject, it may be helpful to recall some course with which you yourself had to struggle in college. Light was shed on this by Thomas Young: [11]

> *"The most difficult thing for a teacher is to recollect how much it cost himself to learn and to accommodate his instruction to the apprehension of the uninformed."*

SOME CONCLUDING REMARKS

I hope you choose a good text for your course; many fine ones are available. But remember that you, not the book, should be the anchor of the course. To many students, the printed word is almost sacred; the text is the final authority. Anthony P. French tells of an incident that occurred in a course in which the text was one of the books he had authored. He writes: [12]

> *"...at the end of one lecture a student came up to me with a question, pointed to a page in the book, and said, 'He says here that...' without the slightest awareness that the 'he' was myself!"*

I have attempted in these pages to set down some guidelines that may be helpful to the first time lecturer. I am a teaching physicist, not a physics teacher. As such, I have tried to share a little pedagogy with you. But be forewarned, a little pedagogy (like a little learning) is a dangerous thing. Some contend that teachers are born, not made, the implication being that we don't really need to learn anything about applied pedagogy. In discussing this "born not made" attitude, Eble [13] compares teachers and athletes. He notes that great athletes are certainly born with potential abilities but that they must develop these through practice. He writes:

"*Potentially great teachers become great teachers by the same route: through conditioning mind and spirit and body, acquiring skills and practicing in respectful competition with great teachers, living and dead.*"

I hope that you will be diligent in mastering these skills, in conditioning yourself, in practicing, even in rehearsing. But always remember that good teaching is more than the diligent implementation of pedagogical techniques. Good teaching is an interaction between student and teacher, a meeting of personalities, a communication of minds. I am reminded in this connection of a comment made by the great pianist, Arthur Rubinstein, when asked to explain the difference between himself and Mr. X, a technically superb pianist who seldom struck a wrong note but did not electrify an audience as did Rubinstein, who hit wrong notes more frequently.

Rubinstein answered [14] in effect:

"*Both Mr. X and I are talented. When we are preparing for a concert, both of us practice diligently day after day. The only difference is that when concert time arrives, I go on stage and make music for the audience whereas Mr. X goes on stage and practices some more.*"

Most of us are run-of-the mill physicists who will be only moderately effective teachers. But whether we are outstanding or merely competent, let us at least go into the classroom and teach physics, not rehearse some more pedagogical techniques. Let us communicate the spirit and excitement of our discipline. Enjoy your year as a first time lecturer!

REFERENCES

1. G.B. Hill, ed. *Boswell's Life of Johnson,* revised and enlarged edition by L. F. Powell (Oxford, 1934), Vol. IV, p. 92.

2. *American Journal of Physics 28* , 568 (1960).

3. Robert A. Millikan, *American Journal of Physics 9* , 82 (1941).

4. G. E. Uhlenbeck, *American Journal of Physics 24* , 431 (1956).

5. Paul G. Hewitt, *The Physics Teacher 10* , 522 (1972).

6. A. B. Arons, *AAPT Pathways* (American Association of Physics Teachers, College Park, MD, 1981), p. 10.

7. *American Journal of Physics 28* , 573 (1960).

8. Cliff Swartz, *The Physics Teacher 18* , 258 (1980).

9. Phillip Morrison, *American Journal Of Physics 32* , 441 (1964).

10. Arnold Arons, *The Physics Teacher 6* , 339 (1968).

11. T. Young, *A Course of Lectures on Natural Philosophy and the Mechanical Arts* (1807); quote is from the new edition by P. Kelland (Taylor and Walton, London, 1845), Vol I, p. 8.

12. A. P. French, *American Journal of Physics 56* , 111 (1988).

13. Kenneth E. Eble, *The Craft of Teaching* (Jossey-Bass, San Francisco, 1977), p. 17.

14. *TIME*, February 25, 1966, p. 85.

CHAPTER 1: TEACHING AIDS
INTRODUCTION AND MATHEMATICAL CONCEPTS

Transparencies:

Figure 1.10:   (a) The addition of two arbitrarily directed displacement vectors.

(b) Using a graphical technique to determine the resultant of the two displacement vectors.

Figure 1.11:   (a) Displacement vector for a person climbing up a ladder.

(b) Displacement vector for a person climbing down a ladder.

Figure 1.13:   (a) Vector addition.

(b) Vector subtraction.

Figure 1.15:   An arbitrary vector $\mathbf{A}$ and its vector components $\mathbf{A}_x$ and $\mathbf{A}_y$.

Figure 1.16:   An alternative way of drawing the vector $\mathbf{A}$ and its x- and y-components.

Figure 1.18:   The components of a vector depend on the orientation of the coordinate system.

Figure 1.20:   (a) Adding two vectors to obtain the resultant.

(b) The x-component of the resultant is the sum of the x-components of the individual vectors. Similarly for the y-components.

(c) The resultant vector and its components form a right triangle.

Problems Solved in Study Guide:

5, 7, 9, 27, 35, 37, 43, 45, 47, 53

Spreadsheets:

#01: Reaction Time
#02: Airplane Flight Times

Demonstrations:

Measurements: Carpenter and Minnix M-016, M-028, M-034;
Freier and Anderson Ma-1 - 3;
Hilton M-1

Vectors: Freier and Anderson Mb-2,3;
Hilton M-10;
Meiners 6-4.7, 6-4.8, 6-4.9

1. Body Language: Help students to develop a feel for metric units by noting the sizes of various parts of the human body. The fingernail of the little finger is about 1 cm wide; a 6'7" basketball player is 2 m tall. Ask students to calculate their mass in kg.

2. Volume: Fill a 1-quart bottle with water and pour the water into a 1-liter pop bottle to show that a liter is larger than a quart. Have students calculate the price per gallon of gasoline when the cost per liter is given. Similarly, have them express a speed in mi/h and in km/h.

3. Time: To give students a feel for time intervals, ask students to keep their eyes closed for 1 minute beginning at the instant you start a large stop clock at the front of the room. Most students considerably underestimate the duration of a minute. Once when I tried this with a class, one student went to sleep and kept her eyes shut for the rest of the hour.

Films:

Meters, Liters, and Kilograms, 16mm, color, 23 min., PERED

Time and Clocks (PSSC), 16mm, b/w, 28 min., MLA

Powers of Ten (Eames), 16mm or 3/4" videocassette, b/w, 10 min. or 25 min., Pyramid

Laboratory:

Bernard and Epp: #1: Determination of Length, Mass, and Density

Preston: #1: Simple Pendulum (Empirical Equations)

Computer Resources for Chapter 1

Programs:

1. *Vector Addition II*. Vernier Software. Apple II. User supplies magnitude and direction of up to 19 vectors. Individual vectors and their resultant are drawn on the monitor screen and the magnitude and direction of the resultant are given numerically. Handy for lectures; also good to drill students. Reviewed TPT February 1986.

2. *College Physics Series, Vol. I: Vectors and Graphics*. Cross. Apple II+. Tutorials on the resolution of vectors into components, vector addition. scalar product, vector product. Reviewed TPT January 1983.

Computer Notes:

CHAPTER 1: LECTURE NOTES
INTRODUCTION AND MATHEMATICAL CONCEPTS

The Nature of Physics (p. 3)

Units (p. 4)

Systems of Units

Definition of Standard Units

Base Units and Derived Units

The Role of Units in Problem Solving (p. 5)

The Conversion of Units

Units as a Problem-Solving Aid

Dimensional Analysis

CHAPTER 1: LECTURE NOTES

Trigonometry (p. 9)

    Basic Trigonometric Functions

    The Pythagorean Theorem

The Nature of Physical Quantities: Scalars and Vectors (p. 12)

    Scalars

    Vectors

    Symbols Used for Scalars and Vectors

Vector Addition and Subtraction (p. 13)

    Addition of Colinear Vectors

    Addition of Perpendicular Vectors

CHAPTER 1: LECTURE NOTES

Addition of Vectors That Are Neither Colinear nor Perpendicular

Subtraction of Vectors

Vector Components (p. 16)

The Meaning of Vector and Scalar Components

Resolving a Vector into Its Components

Vectors That Have Zero Components

Vectors That Are Equal

Addition of Vectors by Means of Vector Components (p. 19)

CHAPTER 1: NEXT TIME NOTES

CHAPTER 2: TEACHING AIDS

KINEMATICS IN ONE DIMENSION

Transparencies:

Figure 2.1:   The displacement vector for a car moving along a straight line.

Figure 2.5:   The velocity of this plane changes by +9 km/hr during each second.

Figure 2.7:   The velocity and the acceleration of this car are in opposite directions.

Figure 2.12:   (a) The velocity of this rocket is decreasing because the acceleration and velocity are in opposite directions.

(b) Eventually the rocket comes momentarily to rest and then reverses the direction of its motion.

Figure 2.14:   (a) A rock and a sheet of paper falling in air.

(b) A rock and a sheet of paper falling in a vacuum.

Figure 2.16:   The displacement y and the velocity v of a freely falling body are illustrated for the first four seconds after being dropped from rest.

Figure 2.18:   Symmetry in the speed of a ball thrown upward and eventually returning to earth

Figure 2.21:   The position vs. time graph for an object that moves successively at three different constant velocities.

Figure 2.22:   The instantaneous velocity at a given time is the slope of the line tangent to the curve at that point.

Figure 2.23:   The velocity vs. time graph for an object having a constant acceleration of 6 m/s^2.

Problems Solved in Study Guide:

5, 15, 29, 31, 35, 43, 49, 51, 65

Spreadsheet:

#03: Objects Falling Freely from Buildings

Demonstrations:

Carpenter and Minnix M-094, M-098, M-104, M-108;

Freier and Anderson Mb-10,13,15,18,21,22;

Hilton M-2 - 5;

Meiners 7-1.2

1.   Acceleration due to gravity: Hold a notebook and a single sheet of paper side by side (in a horizontal plane) and drop them simultaneously. Students usually assert that the single sheet fell more slowly because a larger air resistance acted on it. In fact, the air resistance on the notebook was larger because it had a larger velocity. However, as a percentage of the object's weight, the air resistance on the single sheet was larger. To reduce the effect of air resistance, place the sheet on top of the notebook; be sure it doesn't extend

beyond the edges. Then both objects will fall with the same acceleration. The same effect can be achieved by crumpling the single sheet into a small ball.

Films:
Straight-Line Kinematics (PSSC), 16mm, b/w, 34 min., MLA
Galileo's Laws of Falling Bodies, 16mm, b/w, 6 min., EBEC
Velocity and Acceleration, 16mm, b/w, 12 min., Coronet

Laboratory:

Bernard and Epp:	#7: Uniformly Accelerated Motion
Preston:	#2: Velocity and Acceleration

Computer Resources for Chapter 2

Programs:

1. *The Microcomputer Based Lab Project Motion* (HRM Software) is useful for helping students interpret kinematic graphs. As a student moves back and forth in front of a sonar ranging device, his position, velocity, or acceleration is potted on the monitor of an Apple II computer. Several sonic rangers are reviewed in TPT January 1988.

2. *Motion*. Cross. Apple II+. Generates graphs of coordinate, velocity, and acceleration for one dimensional motion. Has tutorial sections on one dimensional translational and rotational kinematics and dynamics. Reviewed TPT September 1983.

3. *Kinematics*. Vernier Software. Apple II. The student attempts to adjust the motion of a truck across the screen to correspond to a given set of kinematic parameters.

Projects:

1. Have students use the square root finding ability of Eureka or their own computer programs to solve kinematic problems. Nearly every such problem can be set up as one that involves finding the square root of either the coordinate or velocity as a function of time, followed perhaps by substitution of the root in another kinematics equation. Can handle problems involving non-constant acceleration such as, for example, when air resistance is included.

Computer Notes:

CHAPTER 2: LECTURE NOTES
KINEMATICS IN ONE DIMENSION

The Description of Motion (p. 29)

Displacement (p. 30)

Speed and Velocity (p. 31)

Average Speed

Average Velocity

Instantaneous Velocity

CHAPTER 2: LECTURE NOTES

Acceleration (p. 34)

Equations of Kinematics for Constant Acceleration (p. 36)

Applications of the Equations of Kinematics (p. 40)

CHAPTER 2: LECTURE NOTES

Freely Falling Bodies (p. 46)

Freely Falling Bodies and the Equations of Kinematics

Symmetry in the Motion of Freely Falling Bodies

Graphical Analysis of Velocity and Acceleration for Linear Motion (p. 51)

CHAPTER 2: NEXT TIME NOTES

CHAPTER 3: TEACHING AIDS
KINEMATICS IN TWO DIMENSIONS

Transparencies:

Figure 3.1:   The displacement vector for a car moving along a curved path.
Figure 3.2:   The velocity **v** and its vector components for a car moving along a curved path.
Figure 3.8:   A package dropped by a plane in flight is an example of projectile motion.
Figure 3.11:   The maximum height and the range for a kicked football.
Figure 3.15:   Two projectiles launched at the same speed, one at 20° and the other at 70°, have the same range.
Figure 3.16:   Relative velocity for a person walking on a moving train.

Problems Solved in Study Guide:

11, 13, 15, 17, 21, 23, 31, 39, 51, 59, 71

Spreadsheet:

#06: Understanding Data (Marbles Rolling Off Tables)

Demonstrations:

Carpenter and Minnix M-158, M-162, M-182;
Freier and Anderson Mb-14,16,17,19,20,23,24,28;
Hilton M-13;
Meiners 7-2.7, 7-2.11

1. Projectile Motion: Place a small iron sheet on a toy animal (traditionally a monkey) and attach to an electromagnet which is at an elevated position (often attached to the ceiling). Boresight a metal tube on the monkey, place a steel ball in the tube, and fire (by blowing or by using compressed air). A trip wire at end of tube opens the electromagnet as ball emerges from tube. A collision always occurs (if the bullet has sufficient range). An interesting variation is to announce that the monkey is still alive, whereupon an assistant rushes forth shooting a cap pistol.

Films:

Free Fall and Projectile Motion (PSSC), 16mm, b/w, 27 min., MLA
Vector Kinematics (PSSC), 16mm, b/w, 16 min., MLA
Projectile Motion, VHS, Beta, or U-matic videocassette, 15 min, color, FHS
Demonstrations of Physics, Vol. I, Motion, videocassette, 39 min, color, VIKAS

Laboratory:

Bernard and Epp: #11: Inelastic Impact and the Velocity of a Projectile (Procedures A and B)

Preston: #3: Two-Dimensional Projectile Motion

Computer Resources for Chapter 3

Programs:

1. *Physics Simulations I: Ballistics*. Kinko's. Macintosh. Plots trajectories of projectiles, with or without a drag force proportional to velocity. Drag coefficient can be constant or depend exponentially on altitude. Excellent for illustrating lectures.

2. *Motion.* See Chapter 2 notes.

3. *Newton's Laws*. J&S. Apple II. F = ma drill problems. Reviewed TPT February 1984.

4. *Mechanics*. EduTech. Apple IIe, II+. Demonstrates vertical fall with or without air resistance, hunter and monkey experiment, planetary motion.

Projects:

1. Have students use *Eureka* or their own root finding programs to solve projectile problems. It is instructive to have them plot the velocity components as functions of time for a projectile subject to air resistance. Consider initial velocities which are both greater and less than the terminal velocity. Also have them study the maximum height and range of projectiles with various coefficients of air resistance.

Computer Notes:

CHAPTER 3: LECTURE NOTES
KINEMATICS IN TWO DIMENSIONS

Displacement, Velocity and Acceleration (p. 63)

Displacement

Velocity

Acceleration

Equations of Kinematics in Two Dimensions (p. 64)

CHAPTER 3: LECTURE NOTES

Projectile Motion (p. 66)

CHAPTER 3: LECTURE NOTES

Relative Velocity (p. 75)

Relative Velocity in One Dimension

Relative Velocity in Two Dimensions

CHAPTER 3: NEXT TIME NOTES

CHAPTER 4: TEACHING AIDS
FORCES AND NEWTON'S LAWS OF MOTION

Transparencies:

Figure 4.3:   The masses of various objects.

Figure 4.6:   Horizontal forces acting on a stalled car.

Figure 4.8:   Newton's third law is illustrated by an astronaut and a spacecraft exerting forces on each other.

Figure 4.12:   The gravitational interaction between two uniform spheres of matter.

Figure 4.15:   When a box rests on a horizontal surface, the normal force changes when someone pushes down or pulls up on the box.

Figure 4.18:   Forces acting on a person standing on scales in an accelerating elevator.

Figure 4.20:   The actual area of contact between two surfaces is much less than the apparent area of contact.

Figure 4.21:   A slowly increasing horizontal force is exerted on a block at rest on a horizontal surface with friction being present.

Figure 4.23.   A moving sled is decelerated by the kinetic friction force.

Figure 4.24.   The tension force in a rope.

Figure 4.27.   A traction device for the foot.

Figure 4.29.   Four forces act on a climbing jet.

Figure 4.30:   Four forces act on a supertanker to produce an acceleration.

Figure 4.33.   Forces acting on a car that is accelerating up a hill.

Problems Solved in Study Guide:
1, 9, 11, 17, 23, 33, 39, 41, 73, 85, 87, 89, 91, 113

Spreadsheets:
#04: The Tower of Pisa Experiment
#05: Falling Parachutists
#12: Launching a Rocket
#19: Pulling a Car Out of the Mud

Demonstrations:

Inertia: Carpenter and Minnix M-222, M-230, M-234;
Freier and Anderson Mc-1 - 5;
Hilton M-6;
Meiners 8-2.2, 8-2.3, 8-2.4

Second Law: Carpenter and Minnix M-278, M-288;
Freier and Anderson Md-2, Mf-2;
Hilton M-3a,d, M-7;
Meiners 7-1.6, 8-1.4, 8-1.8

Third Law:	Freier and Anderson Md-1,3,4; Hilton M-8; Meiners 8-4.3, 8-4.7
Equilibrium:	Carpenter and Minnix M-268, M-272; Freier and Anderson Mj-2, Mk-4;

1. Inertia: An air track is an excellent way to demonstrate inertia. We are so accustomed to seeing objects slow down due to friction that we are amazed when a glider on the air track moves from one end to the other after receiving only a slight push. Most campuses have a game room with an air hockey table; this is the two-dimensional counterpart of the air track.

Films:

Inertia (PSSC), 16mm, b/w, 26 min., MLA
Action and Reaction, 16mm color, 14 min., FA
The Laws of Sliding Friction, 16mm, b/w, 6 min., Purdue
Principles of Lubrication, 16mm, color, 23 min., IFB
A Million to One (PSSC), 16mm, b/w, 4 min., MLA

Can you figure out the rationale for the film's title? Show this film if at all possible. It shows a massive (about 3 kg) dry ice puck being pulled across a nearly frictionless horizontal surface by a trained flea (whose usual employment is in a circus sideshow act). This performance, filmed in 1959, is narrated by its creator, Edward M. Purcell, winner of the Nobel Prize for Physics in 1952 and now (1991) Emeritus Professor of Physics at Harvard. I always tell this to students; they're amazed and amused to learn that physicists really aren't so stuffy. Then I tell them that this originally was part a longer film (the one listed above) that Purcell created and narrated. There is an interesting story surrounding removal of the flea episode from the original film and its release some years later as a separate film. I'll not relate the story here, but if you're interested in knowing, drop me a line and I'll share it with you. I do tell the story to my classes.

Laboratory:

Bernard and Epp:	#4: Composition and Resolution of Forces--Force Table
Preston:	#4: Newton's Second Law

Computer Resources for Chapter 4

Programs:

1. *Physics: Elementary Mechanics*. Control Data. Apple II, IBM PC. Drill problems in collisions, gravitation, satellite motion, rotational dynamics, harmonic motion. Statements of problems are not complete and students must ask the computer for additional data. Helps students think about what information is required to solve mechanical problems. Reviewed TPT May 1986.

2. *Mechanics*. See notes for Chapter 3.

Computer Notes:

CHAPTER 4: LECTURE NOTES
FORCES AND NEWTON'S LAWS OF MOTION

The Concepts of Force and Mass (p. 88)

Newton's First Law of Motion (p. 88)

Inertia and Mass

An Inertial Reference Frame

Newton's Second Law of Motion (p. 91)

Units and the Second Law

Free-Body Diagrams and the Second Law

CHAPTER 4: LECTURE NOTES

Newton's First Law as a Special Case of the Second Law

The Vector Nature of Newton's Second Law of Motion (p. 94)

Newton's Third Law of Motion (p. 96)

The Gravitational Force (p. 97)

Newton's Law of Universal Gravitation

The Mass of the Earth

Weight (p. 99)

The Weight of an Object

Relation Between Mass and Weight

70

CHAPTER 4: LECTURE NOTES

The Normal Force (p. 102)

Apparent Weight

Frictional Forces (p. 106)

Static Frictional Force

Kinetic Frictional Force

The Tension Force (p. 110)

CHAPTER 4: LECTURE NOTES

Equilibrium Applications of Newton's Laws of Motion (p. 110)

Definition of Equilibrium

Steps in Solving Equilibrium Problems

Examples of Equilibrium Problems

Nonequilibrium Applications of Newton's Laws of Motion (p. 117)

Steps in Solving Nonequilibrium Problems

Examples of Nonequilibrium Problems

CHAPTER 4: NEXT TIME NOTES

CHAPTER 5: TEACHING AIDS

DYNAMICS OF UNIFORM CIRCULAR MOTION

Transparencies:

Figure 5.1:   An airplane flying at constant speed on a horizontal circular path.

Figure 5.4:   In order to move along a circular path at constant speed, an object must accelerate toward the center of the circle.

Figure 5.7:   The tension in the guideline attached to a model airplane moving at constant speed along a horizontal circle.

Figure 5.8:   (a) A car moves, without skidding, around an unbanked curve.
(b) A passenger in the car slides (skids) toward the outside door of the car.

Figure 5.9:   The forces involved when an airplane (a) flies along a horizontal straight line and (b) executes a circular turn by banking at an angle.

Figure 5.10:   The forces that act on a car traveling at constant speed along a horizontal circular path on a frictionless banked road.

Figure 5.11:   A satellite in circular orbit around the earth.

Figure 5.12:   A synchronous satellite orbits the earth in a circular path that is in the plane of the equator.

Figure 5.13:   Apparent weightlessness: (a) a person in a freely falling elevator and (b) an astronaut in a space station in orbit around the earth.

Figure 5.14:   Artificial gravity produced by a rotating space station.

Figure 5.15:   The forces that act on a "daredevil" motorcyclist as he or she performs a loop-the-loop on a vertical circular track.

Problems Solved in Study Guide:

5, 9, 17, 23, 35, 39, 43, 53, 57

Spreadsheets:

#07: Ferris Wheel Rides
#13: Inserting a Rocket into Orbit

Demonstrations:

Carpenter and Minnix M-198, M-354, M-362;
Freier and Anderson Mf-1 2, Mj-2, Mk-4;
Hilton M-3a,d, M-7c, M-16b,f;
Meiners 7-1.6, 8-1.4, 8-2.5

Films:

Inertial Forces, Translational Acceleration, S8, color, 3 min., Kalmia
Inertial Forces, Centripetal Acceleration, S8, color, 3 min., Kalmia
Accelerated Motion and Angle of Lean, 3/4" videocassette, color, 9 min, NTSU

Frames of Reference (PSSC), 16mm b/w, 28 min., MLA

This is THE classic film among physics instruction films; it's the MONA LISA. Made in 1959 by two Canadian physicists (University of Toronto), it immediately became a hit and remains so to this day. If you have time for only one film, this is the one. In fact, if you have time for no films at all, show this anyway. I routinely show about two-thirds of this movie to my theoretical mechanics class (seniors and beginning graduate students). Yes, they do snicker upon noticing that the film byline indicates that it was made for a high school physics course but at least they make an effort to conceal their smirks. Some of my esteemed colleagues do the former but, alas, not the latter. You look at the movie and judge whether it's worth fifteen minutes of class time in theoretical mechanics. I'd be interested in hearing your opinion.

Laboratory:

Bernard and Epp: 13: Centripetal Force

Computer Resources for Chapter 5

Programs:

1. *Mechanics.* See notes for Chapter 3.
2. *Physics Simulations I: Kepler.* Kinko's. Macintosh. Plots orbits of one or two planets, with parameters set by user. Use to illustrate lectures or ask students to look at some interesting orbits.
3. *Physics: Elementary Mechanics.* See notes for Chapter 4.
4. *Sir Issac Newton's Games.* Sunburst. Apple II, IBM PC, Tandy 1000. These games, involving a puck moving on various surfaces, help students develop a good feel for centripetal force, gravitation, friction, and momentum.

Computer Notes:

CHAPTER 5: LECTURE NOTES
DYNAMICS OF UNIFORM CIRCULAR MOTION

Uniform Circular Motion (p. 138)

Centripetal Acceleration (p. 139)

Centripetal Force (p. 141)

CHAPTER 5: LECTURE NOTES

Banked Curves (p. 145)

Satellites in Circular Orbits (p. 146)

The Relation Between Orbital Radius and Orbital Speed

The Period of the Satellite

CHAPTER 5: LECTURE NOTES

Apparent Weightlessness and Artificial Gravity (p. 148)

Vertical Circular Motion (p. 150)

CHAPTER 5: NEXT TIME NOTES

CHAPTER 6: TEACHING AIDS

WORK AND ENERGY

Transparencies:

Figure 6.2:	Work done by a woman who pulls on a luggage carrier with a constant force at an angle Θ to the displacement.
Figure 6.3:	The bench press: A weight lifter raises and lowers a barbell, alternately doing positive and negative work on the barbell.
Figure 6.4:	The forces acting on a bicycle traveling (a) downhill and (b) uphill.
Figure 6.6:	When a constant net force acts on an airplane accelerating down a runway, the work done by the net force increases the kinetic energy of the plane.
Figure 6.8:	Forces acting on a skier coasting downhill.
Figure 6.9:	The gravitational force on a satellite in (a) a circular orbit and (b) an elliptical orbit.
Figure 6.15:	A bobsled zooming down its track (run) is used to discuss conservation of mechanical energy.
Figure 6.18:	A person reaches the water by letting go of a swinging rope on the (a) downward and (b) upward part of the swing.
Figure 6.23:	Work done by a variable force.
Figure 6.24(b):	A plot of force component vs. distance as the bowstring of a compound bow is drawn back.

Problems Solved in Study Guide:

9, 11, 19, 23, 25, 29, 31, 37, 41, 43, 47, 69, 81

Spreadsheets:

#09: A Jet Airplane Landing
#10: The Stopping Distance of Cars

Demonstrations:

Work:	Freier and Anderson Mv-1
Power:	Freier and Anderson Mv-2
Conservation of Energy:	Carpenter and Minnix M-406, M-414, M-418;
	Freier and Anderson Mn-1 - 3, 6;
	Hilton M-14a, b, e;
	Meiners 9-1.3

1. Push the Wall: In my class I go over to the wall and push on it. Everyone agrees that the wall did not move (after all, I'm not Samson); they also agree that you can get very tired if you push on the wall for a while. But if there's no displacement of the wall, there is no work. Sometimes I'll leave this paradox with

them until the next class, at which time I take a bow and arrow and prepare to shoot. With a little coaxing, they concede that I'm quivering slightly and so the bow is moving--so was the wall, etc.

Films:

Conservation of Energy (PSSC), 16mm, b/w, 27 min., MLA
Energy and Work (PSSC), 16mm, b/w, 28 min., MLA
Perpetual Motion, 16mm, color, 11 min., BFA
Gravitational Potential Energy; Kinetic Energy; Conservation of Energy:
 Pole Vault; S8, color, 3 min. each, Kalmia

Laboratory:

Bernard and Epp: #9: Work, Energy, and Friction
                      #10: Mechanical Advantage and Efficiency of Simple
                           Machines
Preston: #6: Conservation of Mechanical Energy

Computer Resources for Chapter 6

Programs:

1. *Work and Energy.* J&S. Apple II. Drill problems on computation of work, work-energy theorem, and conservation of energy.

2. *Physics 1: Module F. Work, Kinetic Energy, and Power.* Control Data. Apple II or IBM PC. Tutorial.

3. *Work, Energy, and Power.* Merlan. Apple II. Tutorial.

Computer Notes:

CHAPTER 6: LECTURE NOTES
WORK AND ENERGY

Work (p. 160)

Work Done by a Constant Force That Points in the Direction of The Motion

Work Done by a Constant Force that Points at an Angle to the Direction of Motion

Positive and Negative Work

The Work-Energy Theorem and Kinetic Energy (p. 164)

CHAPTER 6: LECTURE NOTES

Gravitational Potential Energy (p. 168)

Work Done by the Force of Gravity

Gravitational Potential Energy

Conservative Forces and Nonconservative Forces (p. 171)

Conservative Forces

Nonconservative Forces

The Work-Energy Theorem

CHAPTER 6: LECTURE NOTES

The Conservation of Mechanical Energy (p. 173)

Nonconservative Forces and the Work-Energy Theorem (p. 179)

Power (p. 181)

Other Forms of Energy and the Conservation of Energy (p. 182)

Work Done By a Variable Force (p. 183)

CHAPTER 6: NEXT TIME NOTES

CHAPTER 7: TEACHING AIDS

IMPULSE AND MOMENTUM

Transparencies:

Figure 7.1:   A bat exerts a force on a baseball, thereby changing the ball's velocity (and its momentum).

Figure 7.2:   Raindrops and hailstones hitting a car roof.

Figure 7.3:   Two balls collide and thereby illustrate (1) the forces involved in the collision and (2) the changes in velocity produced by these forces.

Figure 7.4:   Collisions of billiard balls.

Figure 7.5:   Freight cars collide and couple together.

Figure 7.6:   Assuming no friction, two ice skaters starting from rest (and thus having zero total momentum) push off from each other and move in opposite directions at velocities that produce zero total momentum.

Figure 7.9:   Three different objects dropped onto three different surfaces rebound to different heights, thereby illustrating elastic, inelastic, and completely inelastic collisions.

Figure 7.11:   (a) An overhead view of the collision of two balls and (b) a drawing that shows the x- and y-components of the velocity of ball #1 after the collision.

Problems Solved in Study Guide:

3, 5, 9, 11, 23, 25, 29, 35, 57, 59

Spreadsheets:

#14: Small Cars Colliding #15: A Bouncing Golf Ball

Demonstrations:

Carpenter and Minnix M-550, M-562, M-566;
Freier and Anderson Mg-4,5, Mh-1 - 5, Mi-2;
Hilton M-15;
Meiners 9-4.19

1.   The Egg Hits the Sheet: Have two students with long arms grasp the corners of a bed sheet, hold it vertically, and then move the lower hands slightly forward and upward. This forms a pocket at the bottom and also assures that the sheet is not taut. Have a student stand a few feet in front of the sheet and throw a raw egg (that has no cracks, even hairline ones) so as to hit the sheet near the middle. Even if the egg is hurled by a major league pitcher, it is most unlikely to break. In presenting this demonstration, I once had a student who missed the sheet entirely (and, I suspect, deliberately). Talk about a mess; yuck!

Films:

Collision of Hard Spheres (PSSC), 16mm b/w, 19 min., MLA
Tailgating: How Close Is Too Close?, 16mm color, 11 min., AIMS
Human Momenta (NASA Skylab), S8, color, 3 min., AAPT
Two Dimensional Collisions I and II, S8, color, 3 min. each, Kalmia

Laboratory:

Bernard and Epp:	#8:	Impulse and Momentum
	#12:	Elastic Collision--Momentum and Energy Relations in Two Dimensions
Preston:	#7:	Conservation of Kinetic Energy and Momentum in Collisions

---

Computer Resources for Chapter 7

Programs:

1. *Collisions on an Air Track*. Cambridge. Apple II. Chiefly tutorial but includes segments suitable for lecture illustrations. User specified collisions are simulated and in each case a numerical analysis of dynamic quantities (velocity, momentum, kinetic energy) is given. Reviewed TPT September 1985.

Projects:

1. Have students use *Eureka* or write a program to graph the total final kinetic energy as a function of the final velocity of one object in a two body, one dimensional collision, given the initial velocities and masses of the two objects. Ask them to run the program for specific initial conditions and identify elastic, completely inelastic, and explosive collisions on their graphs.

Interactive Videodisk:

1. *Physics and Automobile Collisions* by Dean Zollman. John Wiley, 1984. The disk shows collisions of cars with fixed barriers and two car collisions (head-on, at 90°, and at 60°). One sequence shows the influence of bumper design, others show the influence of air bags and shoulder straps on mannikins. All are slow motion films of manufacturers' tests and many show grids and clocks. Students can stop the action to take measurements, then make calculations of momentum and energy transfers. For most exercises a commercial player is satisfactory; for a few a computer controlled player is required.

Computer Notes:

CHAPTER 7: LECTURE NOTES
IMPULSE AND MOMENTUM

Introduction (p. 196)

The Impulse-Momentum Theorem (p. 197)

Definition of Impulse

Definition of Linear Momentum

Impulse-Momentum Theorem

CHAPTER 7: LECTURE NOTES

The Principle of Conservation of Linear Momentum (p. 200)

Collisions in One Dimension (p. 206)

Elastic Collision

Inelastic Collision

CHAPTER 7: LECTURE NOTES

Collisions in Two Dimensions (p. 209)

Rocket Propulsion (p. 210)

CHAPTER 7: NEXT TIME NOTES

CHAPTER 8: TEACHING AIDS
ROTATIONAL KINEMATICS

Transparencies:

Figure 8.2:   The angular displacement of the take-up reel of a tape deck.

Figure 8.5:   The angle subtended by the moon and the sun at the eye of an observer on earth.

Figure 8.10:   When ice skaters perform the "crack-the-whip" stunt, each skater along the radial line moves along a circle at a speed determined by his or her distance from the innermost skater.

Figure 8.13:   A model plane undergoing (a) uniform circular motion and (b) nonuniform circular motion.

Figure 8.15:   (a) As an automobile moves with a linear speed, its tires rolls along the ground.

(b) If the tires roll without slipping, the distance through which an axle moves is equal to the length of the circular arc traveled by a point on the outer edge of a tire.

Figure 8.16:   Comparing the motion of a tire rolling without slipping to the motion of the tread of a moving tank.

Figure 8.17:   The angular velocity of a rotating object points along the axis of rotation.

Problems Solved in Study Guide:

15, 17, 25, 27, 39, 41, 43, 57, 59, 71, 73

Spreadsheet:

#16: The Rotational Speed of Compact Discs

Demonstrations:

Freier and Anderson Mb-4,10,30, Mr-4;
Hilton M-16a;
Meiners 12-2.1

1.   A Lifetime Going Around in Circles: Ask the class: "Do you know people who just go around in circles?" Then remind them that all of us rotating on planet earth are going around on (or along) a circle. (Ignore the earth going around the sun for now.) How many rev/day? How many rad/day? How many rad/sec?. Then perhaps repeat these questions (calculations) for the earth's orbit around the sun.

2. Linear and Angular Speeds: See #1 above. Ask how fast a point on the earth's equator is moving. Sadly, almost no one will know. How far is it around the earth at the equator? And how much time does it take to go all the way around? So we get approximately 1000 mi/h. They'll be amazed.

Films: None

Laboratory: None suggested

Computer Resources for Chapter 8

Programs:
1. *Motion*. See notes for Chapter 2.

Projects:
1. Ask students to use *Eureka* or their own root finding programs to solve rotational kinematic problems.

Computer Notes:

CHAPTER 8: LECTURE NOTES
ROTATIONAL KINEMATICS

Rotational Motion and Angular Displacement (p. 220)

Angular Velocity and Angular Acceleration (p. 222)

Angular Velocity

Angular Acceleration

CHAPTER 8: LECTURE NOTES

The Equations of Rotational Kinematics (p. 225)

Angular Variables and Tangential Variables (p. 228)

Centripetal Acceleration and Tangential Acceleration (p. 230)

CHAPTER 8: LECTURE NOTES

Rolling Motion (p. 231)

The Vector Nature of Angular Variables (p. 233)

CHAPTER 8: NEXT TIME NOTES

CHAPTER 9: TEACHING AIDS
ROTATIONAL DYNAMICS

Transparencies:

Figure 9.1:   (a) Translational motion.
               (b) Combined translational and rotational motion.
Figure 9.3:   The line of action and lever arm for a force applied (a) perpendicular to a door and (b) at an angle with respect to the door.
Figure 9.9:   The forces and lever arms involved when the fully extended, horizontal arm of a person supports a dumbbell.
Figure 9.11:   A system of objects can be balanced by applying an external force at the center of gravity.
Figure 9.16:   The internal forces which the particles of a rigid object exert on one another.
Figure 9.19:   Using a motor and pulley arrangement to lift a crate.
Figure 9.23:   A solid cylinder and a hollow cylinder rolling down an incline.
Figure 9.24:   An ice skater performing a pirouette illustrates conservation of angular momentum.
Figure 9.25:   A satellite orbiting the earth has constant angular momentum.

Problems Solved in Study Guide:

7, 11, 17, 19, 25, 31, 47, 53, 63, 73, 75

Spreadsheets:

#11: Center of Mass #17: Diving from a High Board #18: Forces in Limbs

Demonstrations:

Torque: Carpenter and Minnix M-614, M-622;
                            Freier and Anderson Mo-5;
                            Meiners 12-4.9
Free Fall Paradox: Hilton M-19k
Rotational Dynamics: Carpenter and Minnix M-662, M-670, M-682;
                            Freier and Anderson Fs-7, Mo-3, Ms-6,7, Mt-5,6;
                            Hilton M-10d;
                            Meiners 12-4.3, 12-5.2
Angular Momentum: Carpenter and Minnix M-768, M-772;
                            Freier and Anderson Mt-1 - 4,6,7, Mu-1;
                            Hilton M-8b, M-19i;
                            Meiners 12-3.1
Gyroscope: Freier and Anderson Mu-2 - 18;
                            Hilton M-19a,b,f,g,h

Conservation of Energy: Carpenter and Minnix M-646, M-650;
Freier and Anderson Mr-1,5, Ms-1,2,3;
Hilton M-19c

Moment of Inertia: Freier and Anderson Ms-4;
Meiners 12-3.3

Films:

Angular Momentum: A Vector Quantity (PSSC), 16mm, b/w, 27 min., MLA Gyroscopes in Space, 16mm color, 14 min., NASA Conservation Laws in Zero-G, 16mm color, 18 min., NASA Games Astronauts Play; Acrobatic Astronauts, S8, color, 4 min. each, AAPT

Laboratory:

Bernard and Epp: #5: Balanced Torques and Center of Gravity
#6: Equilibrium of a Crane
#14: Moment of Inertia

Preston: #8: Bicycles, Boomerang, and Gyroscope

Computer Resources for Chapter 9

Programs:

1. *Statics*. *Cross*. Apple II+. Tutorial on solving equilibrium problems; examples; problems for students to solve. Reviewed TPT February 1983.

Computer Notes:

CHAPTER 9: LECTURE NOTES
ROTATIONAL DYNAMICS

Forces and Torques Acting on Rigid Objects (p. 244)

Translational and Rotational Motion

Definition of Torque

Rigid Objects in Equilibrium (p. 246)

Equilibrium

The Axis Used for Calculating Torques Is Arbitrary

CHAPTER 9: LECTURE NOTES

Determination of the Lever Arms

Selecting the Directions of the Forces in the Free-Body Diagram

Center of Gravity (p. 252)

Newton's Second Law for Rotational Motion About a Fixed Axis (p. 255)

CHAPTER 9: LECTURE NOTES

Rotational Work and Energy (p. 261)

Rotational Work

Rotational Kinetic Energy

Angular Momentum (p. 263)

Definition of Angular Momentum

Principle of Conservation of Angular Momentum

CHAPTER 9: NEXT TIME NOTES

CHAPTER 10: TEACHING AIDS
ELASTICITY AND SIMPLE HARMONIC MOTION

Transparencies:

Figure 10.2:	Factors that affect the amount of force needed to stretch a solid rod.
Figure 10.6:	An illustration of shearing forces and the resulting shear deformation.
Figure 10.8:	When an object is submerged in a liquid, the liquid presses inward everywhere on the object, thereby causing the volume of the object to decrease.
Figure 10.13:	The restoring force exerted by a stretched (or compressed) spring always points opposite to the displacement of the end of the spring.
Figure 10.14:	A graph of position as a function of time for an object undergoing simple harmonic motion.
Figure 10:17:	Simple harmonic motion is executed by the shadow of an object undergoing uniform circular motion.
Figure 10:19:	Use of the reference circle to determine velocity in simple harmonic motion.
Figure 10:22:	Use of the reference circle to determine acceleration in simple harmonic motion.
Figure 10:29:	When a simple pendulum swings back and forth with a small amplitude, the motion is approximately simple harmonic.

Problems Solved in Study Guide:
1, 11, 15, 17, 29, 33, 39, 43, 49, 55, 57, 63, 69, 73

Spreadsheets:
#21: The Size of Grandfather Clocks
#22: Damped Oscillations

Demonstrations:

Elasticity:	Freier and Anderson Ma-8,9,10,12,13, Mw-3; Hilton M-19j
Simple Harmonic Motion:	Carpenter and Minnix M-876, M-892; Meiners 15-1.1, 15-1.2, 15-1.3, 15-1.8, 15-1.9
Spring:	Freier and Anderson Mx-1 - 4,7; Hilton M-14e
Pendula:	Freier and Anderson Mx-6 - 12, My-1 - 3,8; Mz-1,2,3,6,7,9; Hilton M-14d,f

1. Graphing SHM: Attach a very small flashlight to the end of a spring loaded to give a SHM period of a few seconds. Turn off the class lights, turn on the flashlight, set load into vibration, and walk across the room at constant velocity to simulate a graph of displacement versus time.

2. Untitled: Attach an harmonica to a spring and vibrate (or to a string and swing). Ask: What's this? **SIMPLE HARMONICA MOTION.** NOTE: I picked this demonstration up in April 1988 from Dr. D. Rae Carpenter, Jr. and Dr. Richard B. Minnix from Virginia Military Institute. They are outstanding physics demonstrators. See them if at all possible.

Films:

Simple Harmonic Motion, 16mm, color, 17 min, PSU
Periodic Motions (PSSC), 16mm, b/w, 33 min., MLA
Coupled Oscillators: (1) Equal Masses, (2) Unequal Masses; The Wilberforce
    Pendulum; Tacoma Narrows Bridge Collapse, S8, color, 3 min. each, Kalmia

Laboratory:

Bernard and Epp: #15: Elasticity and Vibratory Motion
Preston: #9: Periodic Motion

Computer Resources for Chapter 10

Programs:

1. *Harmonic Motion Workshop.* High. Apple II, II+, IIe. Simulation of simple harmonic motion. Displays velocity vector, acceleration vector, kinetic energy, potential energy. Damped and undamped. Useful for lectures. Reviewed TPT October 1983.

2. *Physics Simulations I: Oscillator.* Kinko's. Macintosh. Displays a mass in simple harmonic motion, damped or undamped. Plots position, potential energy, and kinetic energy as functions of time.

Computer Notes:

CHAPTER 10: LECTURE NOTES
ELASTICITY AND SIMPLE HARMONIC MOTION

Introduction (p. 279)

Elastic Deformation (p. 280)

   Stretching, Compression, and Young's Modulus

   Shear Deformation and the Shear Modulus

   Volume Deformation and the Bulk Modulus

Stress, Strain and Hooke's Law (p. 284)

CHAPTER 10: LECTURE NOTES

The Ideal Spring and Simple Harmonic Motion (p. 285)

Simple Harmonic Motion and the Reference Circle (p. 288)

Displacement

Velocity

Acceleration

Frequency of Vibration

CHAPTER 10: LECTURE NOTES

Energy and Simple Harmonic Motion (p. 293)

Elastic Potential Energy

The Conservation of Mechanical Energy

The Pendulum (p. 298)

Damped Harmonic Motion (p. 300)

Driven Harmonic Motion and Resonance (p. 302)

CHAPTER 10: NEXT TIME NOTES

CHAPTER 11: TEACHING AIDS
FLUIDS

Transparencies:

Figure 11.1: Air molecules in a tire collide with, and exert force on, the inner walls of the tire.

Figure 11.6: Vertical forces that act on a column of fluid.

Figure 11.10: Blood pressure in the feet and in the heart of a person (a) lying down and (b) standing up.

Figure 11.11: Comparing a pump placed at the bottom of a well with one placed at ground level.

Figure 11.16: The familiar hydraulic car lift is an application of Pascal's Principle.

Figure 11.18: The buoyant force is equal to the weight of the displaced fluid.

Figure 11:19: As an object is slowly inserted into a liquid, the buoyant force increases until the object is completely submerged. If the buoyant force becomes equal to the weight, the object floats.

Figure 11.21: In principle, a single glass of water is sufficient to float a ship.

Figure 11.22: An application of Archimedes' principle: A state-of-charge indicator for a car battery.

Figure 11.32: Fluid flow diagram for use in developing Bernoulli's equation.

Figure 11.35: Diagram showing how a household plumbing system takes into account the implications of Bernoulli's equation.

Figure 11.38: The characteristics of fluid flow cause a moving and spinning baseball to curve.

Problems Solved in Study Guide:
1, 9, 17, 19, 23, 27, 29, 31, 51, 73, 101

Spreadsheets:
#25: Hydraulic Brakes of a Car
#26: Magdeburg Hemispheres
#27: Leaky Water Cylinder
#28: Heart Attack Risks

Demonstrations:

Liquid Pressure:	Carpenter and Minnix F-005, F-015, F-025, F-035; Freier and Anderson Fa, Fb, Fc; Hilton M-20b
Air Pressure:	Freier and Anderson Fd; Hilton M-22d; Meiners 16-4.5, 16-4.6
Siphons:	Freier and Anderson Fe; Meiners 16-4.11

Pressure Gauges:	Freier and Anderson Ff; Hilton M-22b
Density:	Freier and Anderson Fh; Hilton M-20a, M-22a, M-22e
Archimedes' Principle:	Carpenter and Minnix F-115, F-120, F-130; Freier and Anderson Fg; Hilton M-20c, M-22c; Meiners 16-2.5, 16-2.6
Pascal's Principle:	Hilton M-20e; Meiners 16-2.2
Bernouilli's Law:	Carpenter and Minnix F-215, F-225, F-235; Freier and Anderson Fj-1 - 11, Fk-2, Fl-1; Meiners 17-2.5, 17-2.12

1. Buoyancy and Newton's Third Law: Fill a flask to a level of about 10 cm. Place the flask and a metal cylinder of height < 10 cm side by side on the pan of a scale; balance scale. (a) Ask: If cylinder is now put into flask and touches the bottom, will the scale still be in balance? Do it so class can see that balance is preserved. Why? Most students think it's because there's no water between the cylinder and bottom of beaker. (b) Tie a string around the neck of the flask; attach cylinder to other end of string. Ask: If cylinder is now placed into flask such that the cylinder is completely submerged and not touching the sides or bottom, will scale still be balanced? Try it and help class to rediscover Newton's Third Law.

2. Air Foil (Bernoulli): Grasp a sheet of paper (letter size or so) by the two corners along a narrow side. Hold this side just below the mouth and blow across the drooping side. The droopy side will rise.

3. Bernoulli: Attach the stem of a funnel to a compressed air source. Hold the funnel vertically upward and place a ping-pong ball into the funnel. Ask: How high do you think ball will go when I turn on compressed air? As you prepare to turn on compressed air, look upward and note that you are directly beneath a fluorescent light. Move off to the side, saying you want to play it safe. Turn on the air. Do your best to look surprised that the ball is pulled downward rather than being pushed upward.

Films:

Fluids in Weightlessness, 16mm, color, 14 min., NASA
Specific Gravity and Archimedes' Principle, 16mm, color, 11 min., Coronet
Bernoulli's Principle, 16mm, b/w, 30 min., EBEC
Mechanics of Fluids: Introduction to the Study of Fluid Motion, 16mm, color 25 min., UIAVC

Laboratory:

Bernard and Epp:	#16: Buoyancy of Liquids and Specific Gravity
Preston:	#13: Motion of Fluids

Computer Resources for Chapters 11

Programs:

1. *Phys. Software Lib. Disk 15: Continuum Mechanics--Fluid Statics*. Allyn and Bacon. Apple II. Tutorial on fluid pressure, Archimedes' Principle, Pascal's Principle, etc.

2. *Phys. Software Lib. Disk 16: Continuum Mechanics--Fluid Dynamics*. Allyn and Bacon. Apple II. Tutorial on fluids in motion.

Computer Notes:

CHAPTER 11: LECTURE NOTES
FLUIDS

Introduction (p. 314)

Mass Density (p. 315)

Pressure (p. 316)

The Relation Between Pressure and Depth in a Static Fluid (p. 318)

CHAPTER 11: LECTURE NOTES

Pressure Gauges (p. 322)

Pascal's Principle (p. 324)

Archimedes' Principle (p. 326)

CHAPTER 11: LECTURE NOTES

Fluids in Motion and Streamlines (p. 330)

    Steady or Unsteady Flow

    Compressible or Incompressible Flow

    Viscous or Nonviscous Flow

    Rotational or Irrotational Flow

The Equation of Continuity (p. 332)

CHAPTER 11: LECTURE NOTES

Bernoulli's Equation (p. 334)

Applications of Bernoulli's Equation (p. 337)

Viscous Flow (p. 342)

Viscosity

Poiseuille's Law

CHAPTER 11: NEXT TIME NOTES

CHAPTER 12: TEACHING AIDS

TEMPERATURE AND HEAT

Transparencies:

Figure 12.2:   A comparison of the Kelvin and Celsius temperature scales.
Figure 12.3:   A constant-volume gas thermometer.
Figure 12.10:   The elongation of a rod, when heated, depends on the initial length of the rod.
Figure 12.15:   (a) A bimetallic strip and its behavior when (b) heated and (c) cooled.
Figure 12.17:   A hole in a piece of solid material expands when the material is heated.
Figure 12.22:   A calorimeter.
Figure 12.23:   Phase changes that can occur between any two of the three familiar phases of matter (solid, liquid, and gas).
Figure 12.26:   A plot of the equilibrium vapor pressure versus temperature.
Figure 12.31:   The dew point on the vaporization curve of water.

Problems Solved in the Study Guide:

15, 19, 25, 29, 35, 39, 41, 59, 65, 67, 75, 79, 85

Spreadsheets:

#29: Coffee Cooling in a Cup
#32: Mixing Hot and Cold Liquids

Demonstrations:

Thermometers:	Carpenter and Minnix H-010, H-014, H-018;
	Freier and Anderson Ha-1 - 4;
	Hilton H-1; Meiners 25-2.3
Thermal Expansion:	Carpenter and Minnix H-040, H-064, H-068;
	Freier and Anderson Ha-5 - 12, Hm-4;
	Hilton H-2;
	Meiners 25-2.1, 25-2.2
Thermal Properties:	Freier and Anderson Hk-7,9,10
Specific Heat:	Freier and Anderson Hb-1,2
Change of Phase:	Carpenter and Minnix H-220, H-230, H-240, H-264;
	Freier and Anderson Hj-1,4,7,8, Hk-1,3,11;
	Hilton M-5d,e;
	Meiners 27-3.1, 27-3.6

1.   Thermal Expansion. Several simple demonstration devices are available from science supply companies (Fisher, CENCO, etc). Almost all stock the **ball and ring device**. A brass sphere will barely pass through a brass ring at room temperature. Most of my students guess that if the ring is heated, the hole will be smaller and thus the sphere will not pass through--but it does. If the sphere is now heated

(the ring having cooled in the meanwhile), the sphere will not pass through. If both ring and sphere are heated, the sphere will still fit through. If the ring is cooled with dry ice or liquid nitrogen, the sphere will not pass through.

2. Liquefied Gases: Very few of the students entering my college physics course have seen liquefied gases. Thus they are very impressed if a small dewar of liquid nitrogen is brought to class and some simple demonstrations performed. Something as simple as pouring some liquid nitrogen onto the lecture desk. Similarly, putting some chunks of dry ice in a beaker of water will get students' interest. Using two or three beakers with different colors of food dye in the water produces a nice effect.

Films:

Temperature and Matter, 16mm, color, 15 min., MCGH
Heat Capacity and Changes of State, 16mm b/w, 30 min., EBEC
Critical Temperature, S8, color, 3 min., Kalmia
Demonstrations of Physics: Vol. 4: Thermal Effects, videocassette, 30 min., VIKAS

Laboratory:

Bernard and Epp:	#18: Linear Coefficient of Expansion of Metals
	#19: Specific Heat and Temperature of a Hot Body
	#20: Change of Phase -- Heat of Fusion and Heat of Vaporization
	#21: Relative Humidity
Preston:	#10: Temperature

Computer Resources for Chapter 12

Programs:

1. *Phys. Software Lib. Disk 19: Macro-Properties of Thermal Systems*. Allyn and Bacon. Apple II. Tutorial.

2. *Physics Vol. 6: Thermodynamics*. Cross. Apple II. Tutorial programs on calorimetry, p-V, p-T, and V-T diagrams, thermodynamic cycles, heat engines, and molecular motion. Reviewed TPT April 1985.

3. *Heats of Fusion/Vaporization*. Microphys. Apple II. Tutorial.

Computer Notes:

CHAPTER 12: LECTURE NOTES
TEMPERATURE AND HEAT

Common Temperature Scales (p. 361)

The Celsius Scale

The Fahrenheit Scale

The Kelvin Temperature Scale (p. 362)

The Scale Itself

The Constant-Volume Gas Thermometer

Absolute Zero

CHAPTER 12: LECTURE NOTES

Thermometers (p. 363)

Thermometric Property

Thermocouple

Electrical Resistance Thermometers

Thermograph

Linear Thermal Expansion (p. 366)

Normal Solids

Thermal Stress

122

CHAPTER 12: LECTURE NOTES

The Bimetallic Strip

The Expansion of Holes

Volume Thermal Expansion (p. 372)

Normal Materials

The Anomalous Behavior of Water Near 4° C

CHAPTER 12: LECTURE NOTES

Heat and Internal Energy (p. 374)

Specific Heat Capacity (p. 375)

Solids and Liquids

Heat Units Other than the Joule

Gases

Calorimetry

CHAPTER 12: LECTURE NOTES

The Latent Heat of Phase Change (p. 379)

    Phase Changes

    Latent Heat of Fusion

    Latent Heat of Vaporization

    Latent Heat of Sublimation

Equilibrium Between Phases of Matter (p. 384)

    Vapor/Liquid Equilibrium

    Liquid/Solid Equilibrium

CHAPTER 12: LECTURE NOTES

Humidity (p. 387)

Partial Pressure of a Gas

Relative Humidity

Dew Point

CHAPTER 12: NEXT TIME NOTES

CHAPTER 13: TEACHING AIDS
THE TRANSFER OF HEAT

Transparencies:

Figure 13.2:   Convection currents in a pan of water being heated.

Figure 13.3:   Convection currents of air when the air is (a) warmed by a baseboard heating unit and (b) cooled by refrigerator coils.

Figure 13.8:   Conduction of heat through a bar when the ends of the bar are at different temperatures.

Figure 13.9:   The amount of heat that flows is proportional to the cross-sectional area.

Figure 13.11:   In a refrigerator, heat is removed by a circulating cold refrigerant fluid.

Figure 13.14:   Absorption and emission of radiation by a block coated with lampblack and a block coated with silver.

Figure 13.15:   When an object and its surroundings have the same constant temperature, the object emits radiant energy at the same rate that it absorbs radiant energy.

Figure 13.18:   The transfer of energy by convection, conduction, and radiation in a hot water solar collector.

Problems Solved in the Study Guide:
3, 13, 15, 25, 39, 41

Spreadsheets:
#30: The Surface Temperature of the Moon
#31: Hot Rods

Demonstrations:

Convection: Carpenter and Minnix H-160;
Freier and Anderson Hc-1,2;
Hilton H-3a;
Meiners 26-3.6

Conduction: Carpenter and Minnix H-140, H-144;
Freier and Anderson Hd-1 - 7;
Hilton H-3a;
Meiners 26-3.1, 26-3.2, 26-3.4, 26-3.8

Radiation: Freier and Anderson Hf-1 - 5;
Hilton H-3b,c;
Meiners 38-5.1, 38-5.3, 38-5.4

1.   Infrared Radiation: Students respond nicely to the detection of infrared radiation by a thermopile (and its galvanometer) placed near a person's forehead. I ask for three volunteers: a blonde, a redhead, and a brunette. I usually discuss

thermography in medicine at this point. Also the determination of heat loss from a building by taking infrared pictures can be mentioned.

2. Radiometer: This is another inexpensive device that demonstrates the reflection and absorption of electromagnetic radiation to produce a difference in temperature between the white and black sides of the vanes.

Films:
None suggested

Laboratory:
Preston: #11: Heat Transfer

Computer Resources for Chapter 13

Programs:
1. *Thermodynamics I. Microphys.* Apple II. Tutorial.

Computer Notes:

CHAPTER 13: LECTURE NOTES
THE TRANSFER OF HEAT

Convection (p. 400)

Definition of Convection

Natural Convection

Forced Convection

Conduction (p. 402)

Definition of Conduction

Factors that Influence Conduction

Examples

CHAPTER 13: LECTURE NOTES

Radiation (p. 407)

Electromagnetic Waves

Definition of Radiation

Emission and Absorption

The Stefan-Boltzmann Law of Radiation

Examples

CHAPTER 13: LECTURE NOTES

Applications (p. 412)

Insulating Buildings (the R value)

Minimizing the Temperature Fluctuations in Orbiting Satellites

Solar Collectors

Thermos Bottle

Dissipation of Heat by Computer Chips

CHAPTER 13: NEXT TIME NOTES

CHAPTER 14: TEACHING AIDS
THE IDEAL GAS LAW AND KINETIC THEORY

Transparencies:

Figure 14.1:   A portion of the periodic table.

Figure 14.7:   A pressure-versus-volume plot for a compression of an ideal gas at a constant temperature.

Figure 14.9:   The Maxwellian distribution curves for particle speeds in oxygen gas at temperatures of 300 and 1200 K.

Figure 14.10:   Molecules of a gas collide with the walls of the container.

Figure 14.12   The diffusion of a drop of ink placed in water.

Figure 14.13   The zigzag shape of the path of a perfume molecule diffusing through air.

Figure 14.14:   Comparing the diffusion of a solute through a channel to the flow of heat through a bar.

Problems Solved in the Study Guide:
11, 21, 27, 29, 39, 47, 57, 61

Spreadsheet:
#33: Tire Pressures on a Long Trip

Demonstrations:

Kinetic Models: Carpenter and Minnix H-440, H-450;
                    Freier and Anderson Hh-1,2,4,5;
                    Meiners 27-7.1, 27-7.5

Gas Laws: Freier and Anderson Hg-1,2,4;
                    Hilton H-5f;
                    Meiners 27-2.1, 27-2.7, 27-2.8

Brownian Motion: Freier and Anderson Hh-3;
                    Meiners 27-7.6

Films:
Mechanical Energy and Thermal Energy (PSSC), 16mm b/w, 22 min., MLA The Nature of Heat, 16mm, b/w, 11 min., Coronet

The Ideal Gas Law; Boyle's Law; Maxwell-Boltzmann Distribution; Avogadro's Principle; Temperature, Energy, and Thermal Equilibrium; Charles' Law; Graham's Law, S8 or 16mm, color, 3-4 min. each, Kalmia

Laboratory:
Bernard and Epp: #17: Pressure and Volume Relations for a Gas

Computer Resources for Chapter 14

Programs:

1. *Physics Vol. 6: Thermodynamics*. Cross. Apple II. Tutorial programs on calorimetry, p-V, p-T, and V-T diagrams, thermodynamic cycles, heat engines, and molecular motion. Reviewed TPT April 1985.

2. *Animation Demonstration: Animated Particles*. Conduit. Apple II. Illustrations for kinetic theory lectures. The influence of gravitational and magnetic fields are also simulated. Reviewed TPT November 1986.

3. *Physics Simulations III: Gas*. Kinko's. An excellent simulation of gas molecules in a box. Use for illustration of lectures.

Computer Notes:

CHAPTER 14: LECTURE NOTES
THE IDEAL GAS LAW AND KINETIC THEORY

Introduction (p. 422)

Molecular Mass, the Mole, and Avogadro's Number (p. 423)

Atomic and Molecular Masses

The Mole and Avogadro's Number

The Ideal Gas Law and the Behavior of Gases (p. 425)

The Ideal Gas Law

CHAPTER 14: LECTURE NOTES

Boyle's Law

Charles' Law

Kinetic Theory of Gases (p. 430)

The Distribution of Molecular Speeds

Kinetic Theory

CHAPTER 14: LECTURE NOTES

The Internal Energy of a Monatomic Ideal Gas

Diffusion (p. 435)

CHAPTER 14: NEXT TIME NOTES

CHAPTER 15: TEACHING AIDS
THERMODYNAMICS

Transparencies:

Figure 15.9: (a) Isothermal expansion of an ideal gas.
(b) A graph of pressure vs. volume for the expansion in (a).
Figure 15.10: (a) Adiabatic expansion of an ideal gas.
(b) A graph of pressure vs. volume for the expansion in (a).
Figure 15.11: A steam engine.
Figure 15.14: A Carnot engine.
Figure 15.15: Schematic representation of a refrigeration process.
Figure 15.16: The operation of a refrigerator.
Figure 15.17: The operation of an air conditioner.
Figure 15.18: The operation of a heat pump.
Figure 15.19: (a) A conventional electric heating system.
(b) A heat pump.
Figure 15.24: Ice is an ordered system in comparison to liquid water.

Problems Solved in the Study Guide:
5, 19, 27, 31, 47, 49, 59, 61, 71, 73, 81, 97

Spreadsheet:
#34: Atmospheric Pressure
#35: Heat Engines

Demonstrations:
Carpenter and Minnix H-320, H-340, H-395, H-405, H-500;
Freier and Anderson He-1 - 6, Hm-1,2,5;
Hilton H-5a,b;
Meiners 26-4.1, 26-4.5, 26-4.6

1. "Boyled" Marshmallow: This demonstration appeared on the scene about ten years ago--at least that's when I learned about it. Place a marshmallow under a bell jar and pump to get a decent vacuum. Observe the rather spectacular change that occurs when air is admitted into the jar. A couple of suggestions: Illuminate the bell jar so that the class can see what's going on. Another possibility is to construct a small plexiglass chamber with a pump-out and place it on an overhead projector so students can get a really good view.

2. Some teachers have found it useful to show a cutaway model of a four-cycle internal combustion engine. Others use small, working model engines--such as an alcohol-fueled steam engine.

3. Entropy. I put some water in a fairly large beaker. In class I drop some food coloring dye into the water and let the class observe the rather slow mixing. After I shake the beaker to get full mixing, I place the beaker on lecture desk and announce to the class that if the water and the dye separate (i.e., unmix) before the end of the class, there will be no examination in the course.

4. I find that students are interested in the performance ratings of air conditioners and heat pumps. So I discuss these in some detail as time permits.

Films:
Perpetual Motion, 16mm, color, 11 min., BFA
Mechanical Equivalent of Heat, 16mm b/w, 30 min., EBEC
Children at Play (Time reversed sequences), S8, color, 4 min., AAPT
Reversibility of Time, S8, color, 4 min., Kalmia
You Can't Go Back, 16mm, color, 6 min., NCSU

Laboratory:
Preston: #12: Mechanical Equivalent of Heat

Computer Resources for Chapter 15

Programs:
1. *Physics Vol. 6: Thermodynamics*. Cross. Apple II. Tutorial programs on calorimetry, p-V, p-T, and V-T diagrams, thermodynamic cycles, heat engines, and molecular motion. Reviewed TPT April 1985.

Computer Notes:

CHAPTER 15: LECTURE NOTES
THERMODYNAMICS

Introduction (p. 445)

The Zeroth Law of Thermodynamics (p. 446)

The First Law of Thermodynamics (p. 447)

Thermal Processes Involving Pressure, Volume, and Temperature (p. 450)

Isobaric Process

CHAPTER 15: LECTURE NOTES

Isochoric Process

Isothermal Process

Adiabatic Process

Thermal Processes That Utilize an Ideal Gas (p. 453)

Isothermal Expansion or Compression

Adiabatic Expansion or Compression

CHAPTER 15: LECTURE NOTES

Specific Heat Capacities and the First Law of Thermodynamics (p. 455)

The Second Law of Thermodynamics (p. 456)

Heat Engines (p. 457)

Essential Features

Efficiency

CHAPTER 15: LECTURE NOTES

Carnot's Principle and the Carnot Engine (p. 459)

Reversible Processes

The Statement of Carnot's Principle

The Carnot Engine

Refrigerators, Air Conditioners, and Heat Pumps (p. 462)

CHAPTER 15: LECTURE NOTES

Entropy and the Second Law of Thermodynamics (p. 467)

Entropy

Energy That is Unavailable for Doing Work

Order and Disorder

The Third Law of Thermodynamics (p. 470)

CHAPTER 15: NEXT TIME NOTES

CHAPTER 16: TEACHING AIDS
WAVES AND SOUND

Transparencies:

Figure 16.2:	Generating a transverse wave on a Slinky.
Figure 16.3:	Generating a longitudinal wave on a Slinky.
Figure 16.5:	A transverse wave on a Slinky showing (a) graph of vertical position of Slinky vs. distance and (b) graph of vertical position of one point on Slinky vs. time.
Figure 16.11:	Comparing a longitudinal wave on a Slinky and a sound wave in air.
Figure 16.13:	When a sound wave travels through air, the individual molecules of the air vibrate back and forth about a fixed location.
Figure 16.16:	Condensations and rarefactions in a sound wave.
Figure 16.20:	The intensity of a sound wave at various distances from the source.
Figure 16.23:	Direct sound and reflected sound.
Figure 16.31:	The Doppler effect for a sound wave.
Figure 16.32:	Wavelength of sound emitted by (a) a stationary source and (b) a moving source.
Figure 16.33:	The Doppler effect for an observer moving toward a stationary source.

Problems Solved in the Study Guide:
15, 19, 23, 29, 35, 47, 49, 59, 65, 73, 79, 85

Spreadsheets:
#24: Doppler Shift

Demonstrations:

Waves:	Carpenter and Minnix W-005, W-010, W-095; Freier and Anderson Sa-3 - 6, 12 - 14; Hilton S-2a,c,d; Meiners 18-3.1
Doppler:	Carpenter and Minnix W-380; Freier and Anderson Si-1 - 3; Hilton S-6; Meiners 19-6.1, 19-6.2
Speed of Sound:	Freier and Anderson Sh-1,2; Hilton S-3f,g
Human Ear:	Carpenter and Minnix W-0305; Freier and Anderson Sh-3, Sl-1

1. Transverse Waves on a String: Attach to one of the side walls of the lecture room a long (10 to 15 ft) rope (or rubber tubing, or coiled telephone cord, or coiled spiral spring). Shake at the free end to send a single vertical pulse along the rope. Discuss the reflected pulse. Then attach a small flashlight bulb (wired to a small battery). Turn off the room lights and generate another pulse. The up and down transverse motion of the light is clearly evident. Move the free end up and down to generate standing waves. SUGGESTION: Save the full demonstration and discussion of transverse standing waves for Chapter 17.

2. Singing Glass: Use a thin-walled glass; an inexpensive wine goblet works well; fine crystal works better--but I don't use it. Fill about half-full with water. Dip your large finger into the water, and move the finger around the rim of the glass, using a moderate pressure. It's important to move the finger at a nearly constant rate; jerking and stopping give poor results. With a little practice, you'll produce a pleasant tone that is easily heard in a large lecture hall. Note the intricate standing waves on the water.

Films:

Simple Waves (PSSC), 16mm, b/w, 27 min., MLA
Pulses and Waves; Single Pulses in a String (Baez), S8, color, 4 min. each, EBEC
A Look at Sound, 16mm or 3/4" videocassette, color, 30 min., TIME
The Science of Musical Sounds, 16mm color, 11 min., ACAY
Sound Waves in Air (PSSC), 16mm, b/w, 35 min., MLA
Propagation of Waves II: Standing Waves and the Doppler Effect, S8, color, 4 min., DEGR
Demonstrations in Acoustics: Four color videocassettes. Total length 3.5 hours. Has 29 demonstrations in acoustics.
Order from: Department of Physics, University of Maryland, College Park, MD 20742.

Laboratory:

Bernard and Epp: #22: A Study of Vibrating Strings
Preston: #21: Waves

Computer Resources for Chapter 16

Projects:

1. Have students use *Eureka*, a spreadsheet, or their own computer programs to investigate energy in a string carrying a wave. The program should calculate the kinetic, potential, and total energies at a given point and time, given the string displacement as a function of position and time. Use the program to plot the energies as functions of time for a given position. Consider a pulse, a sinusoidal wave, and a standing wave. Demonstrate that energy passes the point in the first two cases but not in the third.

2. *Animation Demonstration: Animated Waves*. Conduit. Apple II.

3. *The Microcomputer Based Lab Project Sound*. HRM. Sound is picked up by a microphone and intensity is plotted as a function of time on the monitor screen. Use this as an alternative to an oscilloscope. It has the advantages that sound patterns can be stored on disk and recalled for later use and two patterns can be displayed simultaneously for comparison. Any portion of a pattern can be magnified for closer study.

4. *Phys. Software Lib*. Disk 14: Acoustics. Allyn and Bacon. Apple II. Tutorial.

Computer Notes:

CHAPTER 16: LECTURE NOTES
WAVES AND SOUND

The Nature of Waves (p. 483)

Transverse Waves

Longitudinal Waves

Periodic Waves (p. 484)

Amplitude

Wavelength

Period

Frequency

CHAPTER 16: LECTURE NOTES

The Speed of a Wave on a String (p. 486)

The Dependence of Wave Speed on Properties of the String

Expression for the Speed of a Wave on a String

The Mathematical Description of a Wave (p. 488)

CHAPTER 16: LECTURE NOTES

The Nature of Sound (p. 489)

Longitudinal Sound Waves

The Frequency of a Sound Wave

The Pressure Amplitude of a Sound Wave

The Speed of Sound (p. 492)

Gases

Liquids

Solid Bars

CHAPTER 16: LECTURE NOTES

Sound Intensity (p. 496)

Decibels (p. 499)

Comparing Sound Intensities Using Decibels

Intensity Level Changes and Loudness Changes

Applications of Sound (p. 502)

Sonar

Ultrasound in Medicine

Ultrasonic Cleaners

CHAPTER 16: LECTURE NOTES

The Doppler Effect (p. 504)

Introduction

Moving Source

Moving Observer

General Case

Doppler Flow Meter

The Sensitivity of the Human Ear (p. 510)

CHAPTER 16: NEXT TIME NOTES

CHAPTER 17: TEACHING AIDS

THE PRINCIPLE OF LINEAR SUPERPOSITION AND INTERFERENCE PHENOMENA

Transparencies:

Figure 17.4:	Construction interference of sound waves.
Figure 17.6:	Destructive interference of sound waves.
Figure 17.7:	An application of destructive interference: noise canceling headphones.
Figure 17.11:	Diffraction of a sound wave around the edges of a doorway.
Figure 17.16:	Two tuning forks having slightly different frequencies will produce beats when they are sounded simultaneously.
Figure 17.17:	A 10-Hz "sound" wave and combines with a 12-Hz "sound" wave to produce a wave with a beat frequency of 2 Hz.
Figure 17.19:	Standing wave patterns on a string fixed at both ends.
Figure 17.22:	The spacing between frets on the neck of a guitar.
Figure 17.23:	A longitudinal standing wave on a Slinky.
Figure 17.24:	A pictorial representation of longitudinal waves (1) on a Slinky and (2) in a tube of air open at both ends.
Figure 17.26:	A pictorial representation of longitudinal standing waves (1) on a Slinky and (2) in a tube of air open only at one end.
Figure 17.27:	A complex sound wave produced by combining the first six harmonics.

Problems Solved in the Study Guide:

5, 9, 23, 33, 43, 49, 59

Spreadsheets:

#20: The Tacoma Narrows Bridge
#23: Singing Rods

Demonstrations:

Beats:	Freier and Anderson Si-4 - 6; Hilton S-5; Meiners 19-5.4, 19-5.5
Standing Transverse Waves:	Carpenter and Minnix W-105, W-145, W-150, W-170; Freier and Anderson Sa-8; Hilton S-4b; Meiners 18-5.6, 18-5.7, 18-7.1
Standing Longitudinal Waves:	Carpenter and Minnix W-210, W-230, W-260; Freier and Anderson Sa-17,18, Se-1 - 5,8 - 11; Hilton S-2h, S-4c; Meiners 19-3.1, 19-3.3, 19-3.4, 19-3.5
Interference in Sound:	Carpenter and Minnix W-325, W-330, W-335; Freier and Anderson Sl-3;

	Meiners 19-4.10, 19-5.2
Harmonics:	Freier and Anderson Sj-2 - 6;
	Hilton S-7a,b,c,d,f

Films:

Standing Waves and the Principle of Superposition, 16mm or videocassette, color, 11 min., EBEC

The Music of Sound, 16mm, color, 15 min., Pyramid

Propagation of Waves III: Interference, S8, color, 7 min., DEGR

Standing Waves on a String; Standing Waves in a Gas; Vibrations of a Drum; Vibrations of a Metal Plate; Vibrations of a Rubber Hose; Tacoma Narrows Bridge Collapse, S8, color, 3-4 min. each, Kalmia

Dynamic response of a Suspension Bridge, S8, color, 3.5 min., AAPT

Laboratory:

Bernard and Epp:	#23: Velocity of Sound in Air--Resonance-Tube Method
	#24: Velocity of Sound in a Metal--Kundt's-Tube Method

Computer Resources for Chapter 17

Programs:

1. *Physics Disk 2: Waves*. 6502 Program Exchange. Apple II. Simulations useful for lectures include the reflection of a pulse at a fixed and at a free end of a string, superposition of two sine waves, standing waves, and beats. Reviewed TPT September 1986.

2. *Wave Addition II*. Vernier. Apple II. Simulation of the addition of two waves. In some segments the user chooses the parameters of the second wave. Useful as a lecture demonstration of beats and interference effects. Can also be used to demonstrate Fourier synthesis of sawtooth, square, and triangular waves. Reviewed TPT February 1986.

3. *Animation Demonstration: Animated Waves*. Conduit. Apple II. Simulations which can be used to illustrate lectures on standing waves, traveling pulses, Doppler effect for sound, group velocity, and relativistic e-m waves. Reviewed TPT November 1986.

Interactive Videodisk:

1. The Puzzle of the Tacoma Narrows Bridge Collapse by R.G. Fuller, D.A. Zollman, and T.C. Campbell. Wiley. This videodisk shows the film of the collapse of the bridge. It allows the students to select various demonstration experiments, which are then shown and used to investigate standing waves, resonance phenomena, and the effect of wind on the bridge.

Computer Notes:

CHAPTER 17: LECTURE NOTES

THE PRINCIPLE OF LINEAR SUPERPOSITION AND INTERFERENCE PHENOMENA

The Principle of Linear Superposition (p. 522)

Constructive and Destructive Interference of Sound Waves (p. 523)

Constructive Interference

Destructive Interference

CHAPTER 17: LECTURE NOTES

Diffraction (p. 527)

Beats (p. 530)

Transverse Standing Waves (p. 532)

Generating Standing Waves

Resonance and Standing Waves

CHAPTER 17: LECTURE NOTES

Longitudinal Standing Waves (p. 536)

    The Nature of a Longitudinal Standing Wave

    Longitudinal Standing Waves in Air Columns

        Tube Open at Both Ends

        Tube Open at Only One End

Complex Sound Waves (p. 539)

CHAPTER 17: NEXT TIME NOTES

CHAPTER 18: TEACHING AIDS

ELECTRIC FORCES AND ELECTRIC FIELDS

Transparencies:

Figure 18.3:	(a) Two charges having the same sign repel each other.
	(b) Two charges having opposite signs attract each other.
Figure 18.8:	An illustration of charging by induction.
Figure 18.11:	The behavior of leaves in a electroscope.
Figure 18.18:	The force exerted on a point charge placed in an electric field.
Figure 18.23:	A parallel plate capacitor.
Figure 18.24:	The electric field lines in the vicinity of a positive point charge.
Figure 18.27:	The electric field lines in the vicinity of an electric dipole.
Figure 18.28:	The electric fields lines for two identical positive point charges.
Figure 18.31:	A cylindrical conductor placed in a uniform electric field.
Figure 18.34:	A Gaussian surface surrounding a charge distribution.

Problems Solved in the Study Guide:
13, 17, 19, 25, 37, 43, 55, 67

Spreadsheets: None

Demonstrations:

Electrostatic Force:	Carpenter and Minnix E-040, E-060;
	Freier and Anderson Ea-1,2,5,6,8,11,12,15,17,
	Eb-3,4,9,10,12, Ec-4,5,6;
	Hilton E-1a - f, E-5b;
	Meiners 29-1.4, 29-1.9, 29-1.18, 29-1.23
Induced Charges:	Carpenter and Minnix E-085, E-090;
	Freier and Anderson Ea-12,13,14;
	Hilton E-1g
Lines of Force:	Carpenter and Minnix E-065;
	Freier and Anderson Eb-1, Ec-2,3,4;
	Meiners 29-2.1

Films
Coulomb's Law (PSSC), 16mm, b/w, 30 Min., MLA
Coulomb Force Constant, 16mm, b/w, 34 min., MLA
Electric Fields (PSSC), 16mm, b/w, 24 min., MLA
Electrostatic Charges and Forces, 16mm, b/w, 13 min., Coronet

Introduction to Electrostatics; Insulators and Conductors; Electrostatic
Induction; The Electroscope; Problems in Electrostatics; S8, color,
4 min. each, Kalmia
Coulomb's Law; Discharging the Electroscope: Conduction and Ionization;
Electric Field and Induced Charges; Electrostatic Attraction; Electrostatic
Repulsion; S8, color, 4 min. each., EBEC
Millikan's Oil-drop Experiment, videocassette, color, 15 min. FHS

Laboratory: None suggested

Computer Resources for Chapter 18

Programs:

1. *Basic Concepts of Electricity, Series I: Basic Concepts.* Merlan. Apple II+, IIe.
   Introduction and drill on charging by rubbing, current in simple circuits, electric
   potential difference. Reviewed TPT November 1983.

2. *Physics Simulations II: Coulomb.* Kinko's. Macintosh. User gives up to 15
   charges and their positions, then the program displays electric field lines.

Projects:

1. Have students use *Eureka* or write programs to calculate the electric fields of
discrete charge distributions. Have them use the program to plot the magnitude of
the field at various distances from a dipole along lines that are perpendicular and
parallel to the dipole moment.

Computer Notes:

CHAPTER 18: LECTURE NOTES
ELECTRIC FORCES AND ELECTRIC FIELDS

The Origin of Electricity (p. 549)

Charged Objects and the Electric Forces That They Exert (p. 550)

The Separation of Charges

The Conservation of Charge

The Electric Force That Charges Exert on Each Other

Conductors and Insulators (p. 552)

Charging by Contact and by Induction (p. 553)

Charging by Contact

Charging by Induction

The Electroscope

CHAPTER 18: LECTURE NOTES

Coulomb's Law (p. 555)

The Force Between Two Point Charges

The Force on a Point Charge due to Two or More Other Point Charges

The Electric Field (p. 559)

Definition of the Electric Field

Electric Fields Produced by Point Charges

The Electric Field Produced by a Parallel Plate Capacitor

CHAPTER 18: LECTURE NOTES

Electric Field Lines (p. 565)

The Electric Field Inside a Conductor: Shielding (p. 568)

Gauss' Law (p. 570)

    Gauss' Law for a Positive Point Charge

    Gauss' Law for a Charge Distribution

Applications of Electrostatics: Copiers and Computer Printers (p. 575)

    Xerography

    A Laser Printer

    An Inkjet Printer

CHAPTER 18: NEXT TIME NOTES

CHAPTER 19: TEACHING AIDS

ELECTRIC POTENTIAL ENERGY AND THE ELECTRIC POTENTIAL

Transparencies:

Figure 19.1:   An external force does work in increasing the gravitational potential energy of a ball.

Figure 19.2:   An external force does work in increasing the electric potential energy of a positive test charge.

Figure 19.10:   Work required to move a charge at constant speed between two points (1) on the same equipotential surface and (2) on different equipotential surfaces.

Figure 19.12:   The electric field (1) is perpendicular to equipotential surfaces and (2) points in the direction of decreasing potential.

Figure 19.13:   A cross-sectional view of the equipotential surfaces of an electric dipole.

Figure 19.18:   The electric field lines inside an empty capacitor and inside a capacitor containing a dielectric.

Figure 19.19:   Depressing a key on this computer keyboard changes the separation between the plates of a capacitor.

Solved Problems:
7, 9, 15, 21, 27, 31, 43, 51, 65

Spreadsheet:
#36: Electric Potential Near Electrons

Demonstrations:

Charges on Conductors: Freier and Anderson Ea-7,18,23, Eb-7;
Hilton E-1h;
Meiners 29-2.8

Electrostatic Generators: Carpenter and Minnix E-160;
Freier and Anderson Ea-22, Ec-1;
Hilton E-1i,j;
Meiners 29-1.25, 29-1.26

Capacitors: Carpenter and Minnix E-180, E-210, E-240;
Freier and Anderson Eb-8, Ed-1,2,3,4,7,8;
Hilton E-4b,c,d;
Meiners 29-4.1, 29-4.13

Films:

Electric Potential Energy & Potential Difference (PSSC), 16mm, b/w, 53 min., MLA

The Faraday Ice-Pail Experiment; Charge Distribution: Concentration and Point Discharge; The Van de Graaff Generator; Capacitors and Dielectrics; S8, color, 4 min. each, Kalmia

Increasing the Potential of a Capacitor; Polarity; Conductors, Insulators and Capacitors; Variation of Charge with Curvature; A Working Model of a Van de Graaff Generator; S8, color, 4 min. each, EBEC

Capacitor I: Voltage and Force; Capacitor II: Dipoles and Dielectrics; S8, 4 min. each, DEGR

Laboratory:

Bernard and Epp: #25: Mapping of Electric Fields
#36: The Oscilloscope

Preston: #16: The Oscilloscope

Computer Resources for Chapter 19

Programs:

1. *Physics Disk 3: Electric Fields and Potentials*. 6052 Program Exchange. Apple II. Generates field lines and equipotential surfaces for user supplied distribution of discrete charges. Diagrams can be stored for later display. Chiefly for lecture illustrations. Reviewed TPT September 1986.

2. *Laboratory Simulations in Atomic Physics*. Norwalk. Apple II. Simulations of the deflection of an electron by an electric field, the Thompson e/m experiment, the Millikan oil drop experiment, and a mass spectrometer. Parameters are selected by the user. Excellent for illustrating lectures. Some parts can be used in connection with this chapter, some in connection with Chapter 27. Reviewed TPT March 1984.

Computer Notes:

CHAPTER 19: LECTURE NOTES
ELECTRIC POTENTIAL ENERGY AND THE ELECTRIC POTENTIAL

Potential Energy (p. 586)

Gravitational Potential Energy

Electric Potential Energy

The Electric Potential Difference (p. 587)

The Electric Potential Difference Created by Point Charges (p. 590)

The Potential of a Single Point Charge

CHAPTER 19: LECTURE NOTES

The Potential of Two or More Point Charges

Equipotential Surfaces and Their Relation to the Electric Field (p. 594)

Equipotential Surfaces

The Relation Between the Electric Field and the Electric Potential

Capacitors and Dielectrics (p. 598)

The Capacitance of a Capacitor

The Dielectric Constant

CHAPTER 19: LECTURE NOTES

The Capacitance of a Parallel Plate Capacitor

Energy Storage in a Capacitor

Medical Applications of Electric Potential Differences (p. 603)

CHAPTER 19: NEXT TIME NOTES

CHAPTER 20: TEACHING AIDS
ELECTRIC CIRCUITS

Transparencies:

Figure 20.6:	A simple electric circuit: a flashlight.
Figure 20.10:	The voltage output of a typical ac generator varies sinusoidally with time.
Figure 20.17:	Some of the parallel electrical connections found in a typical home.
Figure 20.18:	The water flow analogy of resistors in parallel.
Figure 20.21:	Four circuits that are electrically equivalent.
Figure 20.23:	The internal resistance of a battery.
Figure 20.30:	Circuit diagram representation of a galvanometer.
Figure 20.32:	A shunt resistor is used to enable a galvanometer to measure larger currents.
Figure 20.35:	A voltmeter consists of a resistor in series with the coil of a galvanometer.
Figure 20.37:	In a parallel combination of capacitors, the voltage across each capacitor is the same, but the charge on each capacitor is different.
Figure 20.38:	In a series combination of capacitors, the charge on each capacitor is the same, but the voltage across each capacitor is different.

Solved Problems:

9, 15, 27, 33, 39, 45, 47, 51, 63, 69, 73, 79, 85, 91, 103

Spreadsheets:

#37: The Incandescent Light Bulb
#38: Electric Circuits

Demonstrations:

Ohm's Law:	Freier and Anderson Eg-2, Eo-1; Hilton E-2c
Resistance:	Carpenter and Minnix E-300; Freier and Anderson Eg-1,3,6, Eh-3; Hilton E-3b
Resistance and Temperature:	Carpenter and Minnix E-450; Freier and Anderson Eg 4,5; Meiners 30-1.4
Emfs:	Carpenter and Minnix E-360; Freier and Anderson Ee-2,3,4; Hilton E-3

Resistive Circuits:	Freier and Anderson Eh-1, Eo-5,6,7; Hilton E-2b,c, E-3a,d
Capacitors:	Freier and Anderson Ed-6,7,8, Eo-12; Hilton E-4e,f
Power:	Carpenter and Minnix E-425, E-430; Freier and Anderson Eh-3,4; Hilton E-3g
Wheatstone Bridge:	Freier and Anderson Eg-6, Eo-8; Hilton E-3b
Potentiometer:	Freier and Anderson Eg-7, Eo-3; Hilton E-3c
Kirchhoff's Laws:	Carpenter and Minnix E-380; Freier and Anderson Eo-2
Meters:	Freier and Anderson Ej-6,7

1. A Questionable Demonstration on Heating: Connect a resistor to a power supply and adjust the voltage to a level that slightly exceeds the rated power dissipation of the resistor. It soon will begin to smoke. I'm a bit ambivalent on doing this type of experiment, but it does graphically communicate (a) that electricity produces heat, and (b) that we often need to know both the resistance and the power rating of a resistor.

2. Sagging Wire: Suspend a long wire (one capable of handling 20 amps) a few feet above the lecture desk with the wire horizontal and stretched rather tightly. Connect to a high-current power supply. Wire will sag substantially.

Films

Electric Fields & Moving Media, 16mm or 3/4" videocassette, color, 32 min., EDC

E.M.F. (PSSC), 16mm, b/w, 19 min., MLA

Series and Parallel Circuits, 16mm, b/w, 11 min., EBEC

Capacitance of Capacitor Combinations: Parallel; Capacitance of Capacitor Combinations: Series; S8, color, 4 min. each, EBEC

Ohm's Law, 16mm, color, 6 min., Coronet

Introduction to the Cathode Ray Oscilloscope, 16mm, color, 11 min., EBEC

An Introduction to the General Purpose Oscilloscope, 16mm, color, 23 min., EDC

Laboratory:

Bernard and Epp:
#27: Methods of Measuring Resistance
#28: Measurements of Potential Difference with a Potentiometer
#29: A Study of the Factors Affecting Resistance
#30: The Heating Effect of an Electric Current
#31: Circuits Containing More Than One Potential Source
#32: A Study of Capacitance and Capacitor Transients

Preston:
#14: Electricity
#15: Ohm's Law: DC & AC Circuits

Computer Resources for Chapter 20

Programs:

1. *Basic Electricity*. Programs for Learning. Apple II. Drill on circuits containing batteries and resistors. Reviewed TPT April 1984.

2. *Circuit Lab*. Mark Davids. Apple II. One of four basic circuits can be selected. Light bulbs, switches, resistors, ammeters, and voltmeters are placed in the circuit by the user, who also selects values for the circuit elements. Ammeters and voltmeters then show correct values. Use as a drill or to illustrate circuits in lectures. Reviewed TPT April 1986.

Computer Notes:

CHAPTER 20: LECTURE NOTES
ELECTRIC CIRCUITS

Electromotive Force and Current (p. 615)

Ohm's Law (p. 617)

Resistance and Resistivity (p. 619)

    Dependence of Resistance on Length and Area of Conductor

    Dependence of Resistance on Temperature

CHAPTER 20: LECTURE NOTES

Electric Power (p. 623)

Alternating Current (p. 624)

180

CHAPTER 20: LECTURE NOTES

Series Wiring (p. 628)

Parallel Wiring (p. 629)

Circuits Wired Partially in Series and Partially in Parallel (p. 633)

CHAPTER 20: LECTURE NOTES

Internal Resistance (p. 635)

Kirchhoff's Rules (p. 636)

CHAPTER 20: LECTURE NOTES

The Measurement of Current, Voltage, and Resistance (p. 639)

The Galvanometer

The Ammeter

The Voltmeter

The Wheatstone Bridge

CHAPTER 20: LECTURE NOTES

Capacitors in Series and Parallel (p. 643)

RC Circuits (p. 645)

    Charging a Capacitor

    Discharging a Capacitor

Safety and the Physiological Effects of Current (p. 647)

184

CHAPTER 20: NEXT TIME NOTES

CHAPTER 21: TEACHING AIDS
MAGNETIC FORCES AND MAGNETIC FIELDS

Transparencies:

Figure 21.7:	Right-Hand Rule No. 1: Determining the direction of the magnetic force on a positive charge moving in a magnetic field.
Figure 21.8:	Comparing the motion of a positive charge moving in an electric field to the motion of a positive charge moving in a magnetic field.
Figure 21.16:	The magnetic force acting on a current in a wire located in a magnetic field.
Figure 21.17:	An "exploded" view of a loudspeaker.
Figure 21.19.	The first ship to use magnetohydrodynamic propulsion.
Figure 21.20:	The torque that acts on a current-carrying coil located in a magnetic field.
Figure 21.24:	Rotational inertia enables the coil of a dc motor to continue its rotation even when the current is zero for a short time.
Figure 21.26:	Using Right-Hand Rule No. 2 to determine the direction of the magnetic field produced by a current in a long straight wire.
Figure 21.32:	The magnetic field in the vicinity of a current-carrying circular loop.
Figure 21.42:	Magnetic domains and induced magnetism.
Figure 21.43:	Magnetizing the magnetic coating on the tape of a recorder.

Problems Solved in the Study Guide:
5, 13, 17, 19, 27, 29, 43, 55, 61, 63, 67, 75

Spreadsheets:
#39: High Energy Particle Storage Rings
#40: Magnetic Fields Inside a Square Coil

Demonstrations:

Permanent Magnets:	Carpenter and Minnix B-060, B-115; Freier and Anderson Er-1, 4 - 9; Hilton E-6a, b, c, d; Meiners 32-1.1
Forces on Currents:	Carpenter and Minnix B-015, B-020, B-035; Freier and Anderson Ei-7, 12, 13, 14, 15, 19, 20; Hilton E-7a, b, c; Meiners 31-1.1

Deflection of Electron Beam:	Freier and Anderson Ei-18, Ep-8, 11; Meiners 31-1.8
Meters:	Freier and Anderson Ej-1, 2
Magnetic Fields of Currents:	Carpenter and Minnix B-015, B-110, B-115; Freier and Anderson Ei-8 - 11; Hilton E-7b, d, E-9b, c; Meiners 31-1.17, 31-1.19, 31-1.20, 31-1.25
Magnetic Forces Between Wires:	Carpenter and Minnix B-120; Freier and Anderson Ei-1 - 6; Hilton E-7e, f, g, E-9a; Meiners 31-1.27

Films:

Magnetic Fields and Electric Currents, I, 16mm, color, 14.5 min., BFA

The Magnetic Field; The Field from a Steady Current; Field vs. Current; Uniform and Non-Uniform Fields, S8, color, 3 min. each, Kalmia

Electromagnetic Induction, 16mm, b/w, 13 min., Coronet

Laboratory:

Bernard and Epp:	#33: A Study of Magnetic Fields
	#34: Measurement of the Earth's Magnetic Field
Preston:	#20: Electron Orbits in a Magnetic Field

Computer Resources for Chapter 21

Programs:

1. *Charged Particle Workshop*. High. Apple II. Shows trajectories of charged particles in a uniform electric field, a uniform magnetic field, and crossed electric and magnetic fields. Velocity components can be displayed. Can be used to illustrate lectures.

2. *Laboratory Simulations in Atomic Physics*. See Chapter 19 notes.

3. *Physics Simulations II: Ampere*. Kinko's. Macintosh. Positions and currents of up to 9 coaxial loops are specified by the user, then the program displays magnetic field lines. Use to illustrate lectures.

Computer Notes:

CHAPTER 21: LECTURE NOTES
MAGNETIC FORCES AND MAGNETIC FIELDS

Magnets and Magnetic Fields (p. 660)

Permanent Magnets

The Magnetic Field

Geomagnetism

The Force That a Magnetic Field Exerts on a Moving Charge (p. 662)

The Nature of the Magnetic Force

CHAPTER 21: LECTURE NOTES

Definition of the Magnetic Field

The Motion of a Charged Particle in a Magnetic Field (p. 665)

Comparing Particle Motion in Electric and Magnetic Fields

The Work Done on a Charged Particle Moving Through Electric and Magnetic Fields

The Circular Trajectory

CHAPTER 21: LECTURE NOTES

The Mass Spectrometer (p. 669)

The Hall Effect (p. 670)

The Force on a Current in a Magnetic Field (p. 671)

The Torque on a Current-Carrying Coil (p. 675)

   The Torque

CHAPTER 21: LECTURE NOTES

The Galvanometer

The Direct-Current Electric Motor

Magnetic Fields Produced by Currents (p. 678)

Introduction

The Magnetic Field Produced by a Long, Straight, Current-Carrying Wire

The Magnetic Field Produced by a Loop of Wire

CHAPTER 21: LECTURE NOTES

The Solenoid

Magnetic Materials (p. 688)

Ferromagnetism

Induced Magnetism

Magnetic Tape Recording

Maglev Trains

Operational Definitions of the Ampere and the Coulomb (p. 692)

CHAPTER 21: NEXT TIME NOTES

CHAPTER 22: TEACHING AIDS
ELECTROMAGNETIC INDUCTION

Transparencies:

Figure 22.1:   Current is produced in a coil of wire when there is relative motion between the coil and a bar magnet.

Figure 22.3:   Inducing an emf by (1) changing the area of a coil in a constant magnetic field and (2) rotating a coil of constant area in a constant magnetic field.

Figure 22.4:   A conducting rod moving at right angles to a constant magnetic field. d

Figure 22.8:   The area swept out by a rod moving perpendicular to a magnetic field.

Figure 22.9:   Computing magnetic flux when the magnetic field is not parallel to the normal to the surface.

Figure 22.12:   A clothes drier connected to a wall socket through a ground fault interrupter.

Figure 22.14:   An emf is induced when a bar magnet moves toward a circular loop, thereby changing the magnetic flux through the loop.

Figure 22.17:   Magnetic pickups used on electric guitars.

Figure 22.20:   A prototype electric generator consisting of one loop of wire that is rotated in a magnetic field by some mechanical means.

Figure 22.27:   An electric transformer.

Problems Solved in the Study Guide:

3, 5, 13, 17, 19, 25, 31, 33, 43, 51, 59, 79

Spreadsheet:

#41: Startup Current in an Electric Motor

Demonstrations:

Induced Currents: Carpenter and Minnix B-205, B-210, B-230, B-240;
Freier and Anderson Ek-3 - 6;
Hilton E-8a;
Meiners 31-2.1

Generators: Carpenter and Minnix B-250;
Freier and Anderson Eq-4,5,7, Er-1;
Hilton E-8b, c;
Meiners 31-2.15

Eddy Currents:	Carpenter and Minnix B-280, B-285, B-290; Freier and Anderson El-1 - 6; Hilton E-8d; Meiners 31-2.6, 31-2.7
Transformers:	Freier and Anderson Em-2,4,5,10, Ep-2; Hilton E-11a, b, c, e; Meiners 31-2.2, 31-3.6
Induced Currents--Forces:	Freier and Anderson Eh-1,2, Em-12,13; Meiners 31-2.9
Inductance:	Carpenter and Minnix B-310, B-315, B-320; Freier and Anderson Ek-7, Em-1,8, En-5,6,7, Eo-11, Eq-1; Hilton E-12a,b,c,d; Meiners 31-3.2

Films:

Electromagnetic Induction, 16mm, b/w, 13 min., Coronet

The Concept of a Changing Flux; Faraday's Law of Induction, S8, color, 3 min. each, Kalmia

Lenz's Law; Large Inductance: Current Buildup, S8, color, 3 min each, AAPT

Laboratory:

Bernard and Epp: #35: Electromagnetic Induction

Computer Resources for Chapter 22

Programs:

1. *Faraday's Law*. Microphys. Apple II. A basic tutorial on induced emfs.

Computer Notes:

CHAPTER 22: LECTURE NOTES
ELECTROMAGNETIC INDUCTION

Induced Emf and Induced Current (p. 705)

Motional Emf (p. 706)

The Emf Induced in a Moving Conductor

Motional Emf and Electrical Energy

Magnetic Flux (p. 711)

Motional Emf and Magnetic Flux

CHAPTER 22: LECTURE NOTES

A General Expression for Magnetic Flux

Graphical Interpretation of Magnetic Flux

Faraday's Law of Electromagnetic Induction (p. 714)

Lenz's Law (p. 717)

The Polarity of the Induced Emf

CHAPTER 22: LECTURE NOTES

Applications of Electromagnetic Induction to the Reproduction of Sound (p. 720)

The Electric Guitar Pickup

The Playback Head of a Tape Deck

The Microphone

The Electric Generator (p. 722)

How a Generator Produces an Emf

The Electrical Energy Delivered by a Generator and the Countertorque

CHAPTER 22: LECTURE NOTES

The Back Emf Generated by an Electric Motor

Mutual Inductance and Self-Inductance (p. 727)

Mutual Inductance

Self-Inductance

The Energy Stored in an Inductor

CHAPTER 22: LECTURE NOTES

Transformers (p. 731)

CHAPTER 22: NEXT TIME NOTES

CHAPTER 23: TEACHING AIDS
ALTERNATING CURRENT CIRCUITS

Transparencies:

Figure 23.3:   The instantaneous current and voltage in a resistive circuit are in phase.

Figure 23.4:   In a circuit containing only a capacitor, the instantaneous current leads the voltage by 90°.

Figure 23.7:   In a circuit containing only an inductor, the instantaneous current lags behind the voltage by 90°.

Figure 23.14:   Comparing the oscillation of an object on a spring to the oscillation of (1) the electric field in a capacitor and (2) the magnetic field in an inductor.

Figure 23.15:   The resonance frequency for a series RCL circuit.

Figure 23.20:   Diodes in a power supply convert an ac voltage into a dc voltage.

Figure 23.24:   A *p-n* junction diode conducts easily in one direction but very little in the opposite direction.

Figure 23.31:   The basic *pnp* transistor amplifier.

Problems Solved in the Study Guide:
3, 15, 23, 25, 31, 35, 49

Spreadsheets:
#42: Causing Spark Plugs to Fire
#43: Tuning Your Radio

Demonstrations:

Capacitive Reactance: Freier and Anderson En-4

Inductive Reactance: Freier and Anderson En-3,5

Impedance: Freier and Anderson Eo-9

Series RCL-Circuit: Carpenter and Minnix B-415;
                         Freier and Anderson En-1,2,12, Eo-13;
                         Hilton E-13a

Resonance: Hilton E-13b,c,e

Hi-Fi Circuits: Meiners 33-2.5, 33-2.6

Films:

Electromagnetic Oscillator I: Free Oscillations, S8, color, 3 min., DEGR
Electromagnetic Oscillator II: Forced Oscillations, S8, color, 7 min., DEGR
Brattain on Semiconductor Physics, 16mm, b/w, 30 min., BTL
Minority Carriers in Semiconductors, 16mm, b/w, 26 min., EDC

Laboratory:

Bernard and Epp: #37: A Study of Alternating Current Circuits

Preston: #17: AC Behavior of Resistors, Capacitors and Inductors; Reson

---

Computer Resources for Chapter 23

Programs:

1. *Apple Physics Disk 1: RCL Circuits*. 6502 Program Exchange. Apple II.

Computer Notes:

CHAPTER 23: LECTURE NOTES
ALTERNATING CURRENT CIRCUITS

Capacitors and Capacitive Reactance (p. 745)

Inductors and Inductive Reactance (p. 747)

CHAPTER 23: LECTURE NOTES

The Series RCL Circuit (p. 749)

Resonance in Electric Circuits (p. 753)

CHAPTER 23: LECTURE NOTES

Semiconductor Devices (p. 756)

Overview: *n*-type and *p*-type Semiconductors

The Semiconductor Diode

Solar Cells

Transistors

CHAPTER 23: NEXT TIME NOTES

CHAPTER 24: TEACHING AIDS
ELECTROMAGNETIC WAVES

Transparencies:

Figure 24.3:	The electric field and the magnetic field of an electromagnetic wave traveling along the x-axis.
Figure 24.6:	The electromagnetic spectrum.
Figure 24.12:	Using a transverse wave on a rope to discuss linear polarization of waves.
Figure 24.14:	Polarized light is produced when an unpolarized beam of light passes through a piece of polarizing material.
Figure 24.15:	Two sheets of polarizing material are used to adjust the polarization direction and intensity of the beam that emerges from the second polarizing sheet.
Figure 24.19:	The "on" state and the "off" state of a liquid crystal.
Figure 24.20:	The role played by sheets of polarizing material in the operation of a liquid crystal display (LCD).

Problems Solved in the Study Guide:
3, 19, 27, 31, 33, 39, 55

Spreadsheets:
#44: Doppler Radar Speed Measurements
#45: The Brightness of Light On My Desk

Demonstrations:

Radiation:	Freier and Anderson Ep-4,5,12,13
Speed of Light:	Freier and Anderson Oa-4
Polarization:	Freier and Anderson Om-1,2,7,8,9,10,11,14,15,16,17,18,19, On-2; Hilton O8-a,b,c; Meiners 35-6.2, 35-6.4

1. Microwaves: Microwave demonstration (or experiment) sets are available from several science supply firm (PASCO, CENCO, etc). I suggest that any extensive demonstrations be saved for the optics chapters--except that a few demonstrations on polarized microwaves be used with the polarization of light as covered in this chapter. Using both microwaves and light to demonstrate polarization will help the student to see the unity of electromagnetic waves. Excellent and simple demonstrations of polarized light are listed above.

Films:

Electromagnetic Waves (PSSC), 16mm, b/w, 33 min., MLA
Standing Electromagnetic Waves, S8, color, 3 min., EAL
Measurement of the Speed of Light, 16mm, b/w, 7 min., MCGH
Speed of Light (PSSC), 16mm, b/w, 21 min., MLA
Polarization of Light, 16mm, color or b/w, 11 min., EBEC
Polarization, S8, color, 4 min., EBEC

Laboratory:

Bernard and Epp: #46: Polarized Light
Preston: #23: Polarization

Computer Resources for Chapter 24

Programs:

1. *Physics Simulations II: Radiation.* Kinko's. Macintosh. Shows electric field lines of an accelerating charge in linear, circular, or oscillatory motion. User selects the velocity and can view either the near or far field.

2. *Radiating Dipole.* R. H. Good. Apple II. User selects velocity of moving charge; program displays electric field lines. Animated diagrams display electric field lines for a radiating electric dipole.

Computer Notes:

CHAPTER 24: LECTURE NOTES
ELECTROMAGNETIC WAVES

The Nature of Electromagnetic Waves (p. 769)

The Electromagnetic Spectrum (p. 772)

CHAPTER 24: LECTURE NOTES

The Speed of Light (p. 774)

Experimental Determination of the Speed of Light

Theoretical Prediction of the Speed of Light

The Energy Carried by Electromagnetic Waves (p. 777)

CHAPTER 24: LECTURE NOTES

Polarization (p. 780)

Polarized Electromagnetic Waves

Malus' Law

The Occurrence of Polarized Light in Nature

CHAPTER 24: NEXT TIME NOTES

CHAPTER 25: TEACHING AIDS
THE REFLECTION OF LIGHT: MIRRORS

Transparencies:

Figure 25-3. The angle of reflection is equal to the angle of incidence.

Figure 25-7: For a plane mirror, the object distance and the image distance are equal.

Figure 25-8: A person's full-sized image can be seen using a half-sized plane mirror.

Figure 25-10: Spherical mirrors: (1) concave and (2) convex.

Figure 25.18: Image formation by a concave mirror when an object is placed (a) between the focal point and the center of curvature and (b) beyond the center of curvature.

Figure 25.19: Image formation when an object is placed between the focal point and a concave mirror.

Figure 25-20: One version of a car head-up display uses a concave mirror.

Figure 25.21: Ray diagram for a convex mirror showing formation of a virtual image.

Figure 25-24: The surface of a sphere with an infinitely large radius becomes a plane.

Problems Solved in the Study Guide:
7, 9, 11, 15, 27, 43

Spreadsheets: None

Demonstrations:

Plane Mirrors: Carpenter and Minnix O-100, O-105, O-115, O-120;
Freier and Anderson Ob-1 - 11;
Hilton O1-c,d;
Meiners 34-1.1

Spherical Mirrors: Carpenter and Minnix O-155, O-160, O-165, O-170;
Freier and Anderson Oc-1 - 11;
Hilton O-1e,f

1. Microwaves: See comments on demonstrations in Chapter 24. Using the microwave demonstration apparatus to show reflection (and, for subsequent chapters, to show refraction, diffraction, etc) is very effective. I'd suggest, however, that most demonstrations be done with visible light.

2. Corner Mirrors: My students enjoy looking at images (especially of themselves) formed by two perpendicular mirrors that abut each other. These are easily constructed using 12" x 12" mirror tile mounted onto quarter inch plywood. The third image, the one behind the corner, is reversed left-to-right relative to the image formed by each of the mirrors acting separately. This helps the student to understand what a single plane mirror reverses.

Films:

Introduction to Optics (PSSC), 16mm, color, 23 min., MLA
Sunshine Optics, S8, color, 3.5 min, AAPT

Laboratory:

Bernard and Epp: #38: Reflection and Refraction of Light (the Reflection Part)
#39: The Focal Length of a Concave Mirror

Computer Resources for Chapter 25

Programs:

1. *Optics: Mirrors and Beams*. HRM. Apple II. Tutorial on law of reflection.
2. *Optics and Light*. Focus Media. Apple II. Tutorial on Shell's law and thin lenses.

Computer Notes:

CHAPTER 25: LECTURE NOTES
THE REFLECTION OF LIGHT: MIRRORS

Wave Fronts and Rays (p. 794)

The Reflection of Light (p. 794)

The Formation of Images by a Plane Mirror (p. 795)

CHAPTER 25: LECTURE NOTES

Spherical Mirrors (p. 798)

The Formation of Images by Spherical Mirrors (p. 801)

Image Formation by a Concave Mirror

Image Formation by a Convex Mirror

CHAPTER 25: LECTURE NOTES

The Mirror Equation and the Magnification Equation (p. 805)

Concave Mirrors

Convex Mirrors

Summary of Sign Conventions

CHAPTER 25: NEXT TIME NOTES

CHAPTER 26: TEACHING AIDS

THE REFRACTION OF LIGHT: LENSES AND OPTICAL INSTRUMENTS

Transparencies:

Figure 26.1:   (a) A beam of light directed from air into water.

(b) A beam of light directed from water into air.

Figure 26.2:   The day and night settings of the rearview mirror located inside most cars.

Figure 26.4:   The apparent depth of an object located under water.

Figure 26.7:   Refraction of the wavefronts as light passes from one medium into another medium.

Figure 26.8:   The critical angle for total internal reflection.

Figure 26.13:   Complete polarization of the light reflected from a nonmetallic surface.

Figure 26.14:   A figure showing how a prism

(a) refracts a beam of light,

(b) refracts different colors by different amounts--thereby

(c) forming a spectrum.

Figure 26.17:   A figure showing that the different colors seen in a rainbow originate from water droplets at different angles of observation.

Figure 26.21:   The three standard rays used to determine the location and nature of the image formed by (1) a converging lens and (2) a diverging lens.

Figure 26.22:   (a) Use of a converging lens to form an image that is real, inverted, and smaller than the object e.

(b) An arrangement similar to that in (a) is used in a camera.

Figure 26.23:   (a) Use of a converging lens to form an image that is real, inverted, and larger than the object.

(b) An arrangement similar to that in (a) is used in slide and film projectors.

Figure 26.24:   (a) An upright, enlarged, and virtual image is produced when the object is inside the focal point of a converging lens.

(b) The lens in (a) is being used as a simple magnifying glass.

Figure 26.32:   Using a diverging lens to compensate for nearsightedness.

Figure 26.33:   Using a converging lens to compensate for farsightedness.

Problems Solved in the Study Guide:

13, 17, 21, 27, 39, 43, 45, 55, 61, 69, 79, 99, 117

Spreadsheet:

#47: Simple Lenses

#46: Human Vision

Demonstrations:

Refraction at a Plane Surface:	Carpenter and Minnix O-210, O-220; Freier and Anderson Od-1 - 7; Meiners 34-1.8
Prisms:	Carpenter and Minnix O-205, O-270; Freier and Anderson Of-1 - 4; Hilton O-2b
Lenses:	Carpenter and Minnix O-305, O-315, O-320, O-330; Freier and Anderson Og-1 - 7, 9 - 13; Hilton O-4a
Polarization by Reflection:	Freier and Anderson Om-2
Total Internal Reflection:	Carpenter and Minnix O-250, O-255; Freier and Anderson Oe-1,2,3,5,6,7; Hilton O-2d,e
Rainbow:	Carpenter and Minnix O-280; Freier and Anderson Oj-10; Meiners 34-1.16
Chromatic Aberration:	Carpenter and Minnix O-380; Freier and Anderson Oj-9
Cylindrical Lens:	Carpenter and Minnix O-340; Hilton O-4c
Human Eye:	Carpenter and Minnix O-580, O-585, O-590; Frier and Anderson Og-8, Oi-10,11,12; Hilton O-5b; Meiners 34-2.1
Pinhole Camera:	Frier and Anderson Oa-2,3; Meiners 34-1.10
Camera:	Hilton O-5a
Fish-Eye Camera:	Meiners 34-1.11, 34-1.12
Telescope:	Hilton O-5e,f
Microscope:	Hilton O-5c

Films:

Reflection and Refraction, 16mm, b/w, 17 min., UEVA
Light and Lenses, 16mm, color, 10 min., JF
Transmission and Reflection; Total Internal Reflection; Refraction;
    The Index of Refraction; S8, color, 4 min. each, EBEC
Sunsets and Scattered Light, S8, color, 3 min, AAPT
Light: Lenses and Optical Instruments, 16mm, bw, 14 min., Coronet
Lens Aberrations, I and II, S8 with 35-mm slides, color, 10.5 min. total, DEGR
The Eyes Have It - Or Do They?, 16mm, color, BFA
Image Formation in the Microscope, S8 and 35-mm slides, color, 5 min., DEGR
The Eye: An Inside Story, 16mm, color, 10 min., Coronet
Demonstrations of Physics, Volume 7: Light, videocassette, 30min, VIKAS

Laboratory:

Bernard and Epp:	#38: Reflection and Refraction of Light
	#40: Properties of Converging and Diverging Lenses
	#43: Index of Refraction with the Prism Spectrometer
	#41: Optical Instruments Employing Two Lenses
Preston:	#24: Lenses and Microscopes

Computer Resources for Chapter 26

Programs:

1.   *Optics and Light*. Focus. Apple II. Demonstration and tutorial on Snell's law and thin lenses. User selects the parameters, then the program draws a ray diagram. Reviewed TPT January 1985.

2.   *General Physics Series Volume 8--Optics*. Cross. AppleII. Tutorial.

Computer Notes:

CHAPTER 26: LECTURE NOTES
THE REFRACTION OF LIGHT:
LENSES AND OPTICAL INSTRUMENTS

The Index of Refraction (p. 817)

Snell's Law and the Refraction of Light (p. 817)

Snell's Law

Apparent Depth

The Displacement of Light by a Transparent Slab of Material

Derivation of Snell's Law

CHAPTER 26: LECTURE NOTES

Total Internal Reflection (p. 824)

The Critical Angle and Total Internal Reflection

Prisms and Total Internal Reflection

Fiber Optics

CHAPTER 26: LECTURE NOTES

Polarization and the Reflection and Refraction of Light (p. 828)

The Dispersion of Light: Prisms and Rainbows (p. 829)

Lenses (p. 831)

Converging Lenses

Diverging Lenses

CHAPTER 26: LECTURE NOTES

The Formation of Images by Lenses (p. 832)

Ray Diagrams

Image Formation by a Converging Lens

Image Formation by a Diverging Lens

The Thin-Lens Equation and the Magnification Equation (p. 836)

CHAPTER 26: LECTURE NOTES

Lenses in Combination (p. 839)

The Human Eye (p. 840)

The Anatomy of the Eye

The Optics of the Eye

Nearsightedness

CHAPTER 26: LECTURE NOTES

Farsightedness

The Refractive Power of a Lens--The Diopter

Angular Magnification and the Magnifying Glass (p. 845)

Angular Size

Angular Magnification

The Compound Microscope (p. 848)

CHAPTER 26: LECTURE NOTES

The Telescope (p. 851)

Lens Aberrations (p. 853)

Spherical Aberration

Chromatic Aberration

CHAPTER 26: NEXT TIME NOTES

CHAPTER 27: TEACHING AIDS

INTERFERENCE AND THE WAVE NATURE OF LIGHT

Transparencies:

Figure 27.1:	Constructive interference between two waves that are in phase.
Figure 27.2:	Destructive interference by two waves that are out of phase.
Figure 27.3:	Fluttering of a TV picture due to interference between direct and reflected electromagnetic waves.
Figure 27.4:	The experimental arrangement for Young's double-slit experiment.
Figure 27.6:	Young's double slit experiment: (a) pattern of bright and dark fringes and (b) a graph of the light intensity.
Figure 27.8:	Diagrams used to derive the equation for the angle at which bright fringes occur.
Figure 27.11:	Interference produced by thin films.
Figure 27.17:	Schematic drawing of a Michelson interferometer.
Figure 27.20:	Diffraction of light by a single slit.
Figure 27.22:	Diagram showing how destructive interference leads to the first dark fringe in the diffraction pattern produced by a single slit.
Figure 27.27:	Diffraction pattern produced by a small circular opening.
Figure 27.33:	Diagram showing formation of the first- and second-order intensity maxima by a diffraction grating.
Figure 27.36:	A schematic drawing of the bottom of a compact disc (CD), showing the "pits" that carry the audio information.
Figure 27.37:	Illustration of the three-beam tracking method often used in CD players.

Problems Solved in the Study Guide:
7, 9, 15, 19, 27, 35, 43, 49, 63

Spreadsheet:
#48: Double Slit Interference Patterns

Demonstrations:

Double Slit Interference:	Carpenter and Minnix O-405; Freier and Anderson Ol-4,5,9; Hilton O-7c; Meiners 35-2.1
Single Slit Diffraction:	Carpenter and Minnix O-505; Freier and Anderson Ol-2,3,6,7; Hilton O-7c; Meiners 35-3.1

Thin Film Interference:	Carpenter and Minnix O-455, O-460, O-465; Freier and Anderson Ol-15,16,17,18; Hilton O-7d,e,f; Meiners 35-2.2, 35-2.4
Interferometer:	Freier and Anderson Ol-19,20; Hilton O-2e; Meiners 35-2.7
Multiple Slits:	Carpenter and Minnix O-510, O-520, O-525; Freier and Anderson Ol-10,11,12,13; Hilton O-7g; Meiners 25-3.2
Diffraction:	Carpenter and Minnix O-530, O-550, O-555; Freier and Anderson Ol-14,21,23; O-7g,h,j; Meiners 35-3.7

Films:

Interference and Diffraction (PSSC, Ripple Tank), 16mm, b/w, 19 min., MLA
Joseph Fraunhofer: Diffraction, 16mm, color, 16 min., RPI
Introduction to Holography, 16mm color, 17 min., EBEC
Interference in Photon Polarization, 16mm, silent, color, 4 min., EDC
Shadow of a Hole, S8, color, 3.5 min., AAPT
Diffraction--Single Slit; Diffraction--Double Slit; Resolving Power;
    The Michelson Interferometer, S8, color, 4 min. each, Kalmia

Laboratory:

| Bernard and Epp: | #45: A Study of Spectra with the Grating Spectrometer
#44: The Wavelength of Light |
| Preston: | #22: Diffraction and Resolution
#25: Spectrometer: Balmer Series |

Computer Resources for Chapter 27

Programs:

1. *Light Waves*. Educational. Apple II. Simulations of Young's experiment with user selected parameters. Students can view either a graph of the intensity or a simulated intensity pattern.

2. *Physics Simulations III: Diffraction*. Kinko's. Macintosh. Program shows intensity plots for single slits, double slits, and other apertures.

Computer Notes:

CHAPTER 27: LECTURE NOTES
INTERFERENCE AND THE WAVE NATURE OF LIGHT

The Principle of Linear Superposition (p. 867)

Young's Double Slit Experiment (p. 869)

Thin-Film Interference (p. 873)

CHAPTER 27: LECTURE NOTES

The Michelson Interferometer (p. 879)

Diffraction (p. 880)

CHAPTER 27: LECTURE NOTES

Resolving Power (p. 885)

The Diffraction Grating (p. 889)

Compact Discs and the Use of Interference (p. 892)

X-Ray Diffraction (p. 894)

CHAPTER 27: NEXT TIME NOTES

CHAPTER 28: TEACHING AIDS

SPECIAL RELATIVITY

Transparencies:

Figure 28.1: The position and time of an event are measured by (a) an observer fixed on the earth and (b) an observer in a moving airplane.

Figure 28.3: A light clock.

Figure 28.4: A moving astronaut and an observer on earth measure different time intervals between ticks of the astronaut's light clock.

Figure 28.5: The distance and time for a trip from the earth to Alpha Centauri as measured by (a) an observer on the earth and (b) a passenger who makes the trip.

Figure 28.6: Graph of the (ratio of relativistic momentum to nonrelativistic momentum) versus speed.

Figure 28.10: A spacecraft, moving at a speed of 0.7c relative to a second spacecraft, fires a laser beam toward the second spacecraft.

Problems Solved in the Study Guide:

5, 11, 17, 23, 37, 45

Spreadsheet:

#53: Relativistic Speeds of Electrons in a Linear Accelerator

Demonstrations: None suggested

Films:

Relativistic Time Dilation (Paul G. Hewitt), color. 12 min.; 16mm from SMITH; Videocassette from BAY

The Ultimate Speed: An Exploration with High Energy Electrons, 16mm, b/w, 38 min., MLA

Time Dilation: An Experiment with Mu-Mesons (PSSC), 16mm, b/w, 36 min, MLA

$E = mc^2$, 16mm or 3/4" videocassette, color, 28 min., UCMC

Marking Time, 16mm or 3/4" videocassette, 28 min., UCMC

Motion and Time: An Introduction to Einstein's Theory of Relativity, 16mm, color, 11 min., STERLED

Mystery of Time, 16mm, color, 28 min., MIS

A Relativistic Ride, 16mm or S8, color, 4 min., EDC

Powers of Ten (Eames), 16mm or 3/4" videocassette, b/w, 10 min. or 25 min., Pyramid

Laboratory: None suggested

Computer Resources for Chapter 28

Programs:

1. *Physics Simulations I: Einstein*. Kinko's. Macintosh. The screen is split to show the views of events as seen in two frames which are moving relative to each other. Clocks show time intervals between events. Use to demonstrate time dilation, length contraction, twin paradox.

2. *Intermediate Physics Simulations: Relativistic Motion*. R. H. Good. Apple II. User adjusts the velocity (in two dimensions) of a moving clock, which ticks at uniform intervals and lays down a marker at each tick. The screen shows the time in the observer's frame and in the rest frame of the clock. Use to demonstrate time dilation, length contraction, twin paradox.

Computer Notes:

CHAPTER 28: LECTURE NOTES
SPECIAL RELATIVITY

Events and Inertial Reference Frames (p. 903)

The Postulates of Special Relativity (p. 904)

The Relativity of Time: Time Dilation (p. 905)

Time Dilation

Proper Time Interval

CHAPTER 28: LECTURE NOTES

Space Travel

Verification of Time Dilation

The Relativity of Length: Length Contraction (p. 910)

Relativistic Momentum (p. 913)

CHAPTER 28: LECTURE NOTES

The Equivalence of Energy and Mass: $E = mc^2$ (p. 914)

   The Total Energy of an Object

   The Speed of Light Is the Ultimate Speed

The Relativistic Addition of Velocities (p. 919)

CHAPTER 28: NEXT TIME NOTES

CHAPTER 29: TEACHING AIDS

PARTICLES AND WAVES

Transparencies:

Figure 29.1:   A beam of electrons incident on a double slit forms an interference patterns of bright and dark fringes remarkably similar to the pattern observed in Young's doubleslit experiment.

Figure 29.2:   For radiation emitted by a blackbody, the intensity per wavelength varies with wavelength as shown by these two curves (for different fixed temperatures).

Figure 29.3:   Experimental setup for observing the photoelectric effect.

Figure 29.5:   The sound produced by most motion pictures uses a technique that is based on the photoelectric effect.

Figure 29.6:   The Compton effect.

Figure 29.7:   A solar sail that might provide propulsion for an interstellar spacecraft.

Figure 29.10:   A diffraction pattern of bright and dark fringes is formed by electrons that pass through a single slit.

Problems Solved in the Study Guide:

7, 9, 19, 29, 33, 45, 47

Spreadsheets:

#51: The Low Temperature Heat Capacity of Metals
#52: The Color of a Hot Filament

Demonstrations:

Photoelectric Effect: Carpenter and Minnix S-095;
Freier and Anderson MPb-1;
Hilton A-4b,c;
Meiners 38-2.1

Models of Atom: Hilton A-5a,b;
Meiners 39-5.1

Electron Diffraction: Hilton A-13b;
Meiners 38-7.4

Compton Effect: Meiners 38-3.1, 38-3.2

Films:

 Matter Waves (PSSC), 16mm, b/w, 28 min., MLA
 Anti-Matter, 16mm, color, 12 min., AEF
 Wave-Particle Duality, 16mm, color, 22 min., IFB
 Interference of Photons (PSSC), 16mm, b/w, 12 min., MLA
 Photoelectric Effect (PSSC), 16mm, color, 27 min., MLA
 Photoemission of Electrons, 16mm, b/w, 4 min., UEVA
 Photons (PSSC), 16mm, b/w, 18 min., MLA
 Pressure of Light (PSSC), 16mm, b/w, 23 min., MLA
 The Photoelectric Effect, S8, color, 4 min., Kalmia
 Discharging the Electroscope--The Photoelectric Effect, S8, color, 4 min., EBEC
 Electron Diffraction, videocassette, 15 min., FHS

Laboratory:

 Bernard and Epp: #45: A Study of Spectra with the Grating Spectrometer

---

Computer Resources for Chapter 29

Programs:

1. *Atoms and Matter*. Focus. A series of programs that simulate various modern experiments. One plots radiative intensity vs. frequency for a blackbody at a temperature chosen by the user. This display can be used to illustrate the lecture. The tutorial material can be used by the students. Reviewed TPT December 1986.

Computer Notes:

CHAPTER 29: LECTURE NOTES

PARTICLES AND WAVES

The Wave-Particle Duality (p. 927)

Young's Double Slit Experiment with Light (Waves)

Young's Double Slit Experiment with Electrons (Particles)

Blackbody Radiation and Planck's Constant (p. 927)

How the Intensity per Unit Wavelength Depends on Wavelength and Temperature

Discrete Energies for Atomic Oscillators

Photons and the Photoelectric Effect (p. 929)

Energy of a Photon

The Work Function for a Metal

Application of the Photoelectric Effect

CHAPTER 29: LECTURE NOTES

The Momentum of a Photon and the Compton Effect (p. 932)

Collision Between an X-ray Photon and a Free Electron

Difference in Wavelength Between Incident and Scattered Photons

The de Broglie Wavelength and the Wave Nature of Matter (p. 934)

The deBroglie Wavelength of a Particle

The Davisson-Germer Experiment

Particle Waves and Probability

Quantum Mechanics

CHAPTER 29: LECTURE NOTES

The Heisenberg Uncertainty Principle (p. 937)

The Single Slit Diffraction Pattern for Electrons

Simultaneous Measurement of a Particle's Position and Momentum

The Uncertainty Principle

Position and Momentum

Energy and Time

CHAPTER 29: NEXT TIME NOTES

CHAPTER 30: TEACHING AIDS

THE NATURE OF THE ATOM

Transparencies:

Figure 30.2:   A Rutherford scattering experiment.

Figure 30.4:   The Lyman, Balmer, and Paschen series of lines emitted by atomic hydrogen.

Figure 30.9:   Diagram showing the energy level transitions that correspond to the Lyman, Balmer, and Paschen series of lines for the hydrogen atom.

Figure 30.12:   The electron probability clouds for two specific quantum states of the hydrogen atom.

Figure 30.15:   The maximum number of electrons that the various subshells of an atom can hold.

Figure 30.17:   Schematic diagram of an x-ray tube.

Figure 30.23:   A schematic drawing of a helium/neon laser.

Figure 30.25:   An arrangement used to produce a hologram.

Figure 30.27:   Laser light incident on a hologram produces a real and a virtual image.

Problems Solved in the Study Guide:

5, 15, 19, 21, 25, 29, 33, 41, 45, 59

Spreadsheet:

#49: Rutherford Scattering

Demonstrations:

Lasers: Hilton A-12

X-rays: Hilton A-2c,d, A-7

Zeeman Effect: Freier and Anderson MPc-1;
                    Hilton A-20a

Films:

The Hydrogen Atom, 16mm, color, 20 min., MLA
Absorption Spectra, 16mm, color, 3 min., OHSU
Bohr Atom, 16mm, b/w, 30 min., EBEC
Electron Shell Structure, 16mm, b/w, 30 min., EBEC
A New Reality (The Work of Niels Bohr), 16mm, color, 50 min., IFB
Atomic Structure and the Periodic Table, 16mm, color, 11 min., EBEC

X-ray Spectroscopy, 16mm, color, 26 min., NAVC
Introduction to Lasers, 16mm, color, 17 min., EBEC
Laser: The Light of the Future, 16mm, color, 30 min., INUAVC
The Rutherford Scattering of Alpha Particles, videocassette, 15min., FHS

Laboratory:

Bernard and Epp: #42: The Laser

Computer Resources for Chapter 30

Programs:

1. *Animation Demonstration: Electron Waves in an Atom*. Conduit. Apple II. Compares classical electron orbits and quantum wave patterns. Shows quantization of orbits by applying boundary conditions and simulates radiative transitions. Reviewed TPT November 1986.

Computer Notes:

CHAPTER 30: LECTURE NOTES
THE NATURE OF THE ATOM

Rutherford Scattering and the Nuclear Atom (p. 947)

Line Spectra (p. 948)

The Bohr Model of the Hydrogen Atom (p. 951)

The Model

The Energies and Radii of the Bohr Orbits

CHAPTER 30: LECTURE NOTES

Energy Level Diagrams

The Line Spectra of the Hydrogen Atom

De Broglie's Explanation of Bohr's Angular Momentum Assumption (p. 956)

The Quantum Mechanical Picture of the Hydrogen Atom (p. 957)

Quantum Numbers

CHAPTER 30: LECTURE NOTES

Electron Probability Clouds

The Pauli Exclusion Principle and the Periodic Table of the Elements (p. 962)

Multiple-Electron Atoms

Shorthand Notation for the Electronic Configuration of the Atom

The Periodic Table

X-Rays (p. 966)

The Laser (p. 969)

Holography (p. 972)

CHAPTER 30: NEXT TIME NOTES

CHAPTER 31: TEACHING AIDS
NUCLEAR PHYSICS AND RADIOACTIVITY

Transparencies:

Figure 31.1:	The atomic nucleus is approximately spherical and contains protons clustered closely together with neutrons.
Figure 31.2:	Graph of neutron number versus proton number for naturally occurring stable nuclei.
Figure 31.3:	Disassembling a nucleus into its constituent protons and neutrons.
Figure 31.5:	A plot of binding energy per nucleon versus nucleon number A.
Figure 31.6:	Alpha and beta rays are deflected by a magnetic field; gamma rays are not.
Figure 31.10:	Graph that depicts the half-life of a radioactive decay.
Figure 31.12:	A chart showing the radioactivity decay series that begins with uranium-238 and ends with lead-226.
Figure 31.13:	A Geiger counter.
Figure 31.14:	A scintillation counter.

Problems Solved in the Study Guide:
7, 15, 23, 27, 33, 41, 49, 57

Spreadsheet:
#50: Radioactivity

Demonstrations:

Geiger Counter:	Carpenter and Minnix S-135; Freier and Anderson MPa-2; Meiners 41-1.1
Radioactivity:	Hilton A-15, A-16, A-18; Meiners 41-1.8, 41-1.9
Cloud Chambers:	Carpenter and Minnix S-140; Hilton A-15b,c; Meiners 41-3.5, 41-3.6

Films:
The Discovery of Radioactivity, 16mm or 3/4" videocassette, color, 15 min., IFB
Atomic Physics, Part 3: Nuclear Structure of the Atom, 16mm, b/w, 19 min., UEVA
Atomic Physics, Part 4: Discovery of the Neutron, 16mm, b/w, 22 min., UEVA
Exploring the Atomic Nucleus, 16mm, color, 12 min., Coronet
The Atom and Archaeology (Carbon-14 dating), 16mm, color, 25 min., HFC
Atomic Energy: Inside the Atom, 16mm, color, 13 min., EBEC

Fundamentals of Radioactivity, 16mm, b/w, 56 min., NAVC
Radioactivity Decay, 16mm, color, 3 min., OHSU
Radioactivity, 16mm, color, 13 min., MCGH
The Determination of a Radioactive Half-life, videocassette, 15min., FHS

Laboratory:

Bernard and Epp: #48: The Characteristics of a Geiger Tube
#49: Statistics of Sample Measurement
#50: The Geometry of Radioactive Radiation
#51: Properties of Radioactive Radiation
#52: Measurement of Radioactive Half-Life

Preston: #26: Geiger-Mueller Counter: Radioactive Decay
#27: Half-Life

Computer Resources for Chapter 31

Programs:

1. *SCATTER: Nuclear Scattering*. Conduit. Apple II. Tutorial on nuclear scattering.
2. *Radioactivity: Half-life*. Phizphun. Apple II. Tutorial.

Computer Notes:

CHAPTER 31: LECTURE NOTES
NUCLEAR PHYSICS AND RADIOACTIVITY

Nuclear Structure (p. 982)

The Strong Nuclear Force and the Stability of the Nucleus (p. 983)

The Mass Defect of the Nucleus and Nuclear Binding Energy (p. 984)

Radioactivity (p. 987)

    Conservation Laws

CHAPTER 31: LECTURE NOTES

Alpha Decay

Beta Decay

Gamma Decay

The Neutrino (p. 993)

Radioactive Decay and Activity (p. 993)

CHAPTER 31: LECTURE NOTES

Radioactive Dating (p. 996)

Radioactive Decay Series (p. 998)

Detectors of Radiation (p. 998)

The Geiger Counter

The Scintillator Counter

Semiconductor Detectors

Recording the Path of High Energy Particles

Cloud Chamber

Bubble Chamber

Photographic Emulsion

CHAPTER 31: NEXT TIME NOTES

CHAPTER 32: TEACHING AIDS
IONIZING RADIATION, NUCLEAR ENERGY, AND ELEMENTARY PARTICLES

Transparencies:

Figure 32.2:   A bomb detection system that uses thermal neutrons.

Figure 32.3:   Fission is illustrated by the uranium-235 nucleus that is bombarded by a slow neutron.

Figure 32.4:   A chain reaction.

Figure 32.7:   Diagram of a nuclear power plant that uses a pressurized water reactor.

Figure 32.8:   Fission and fusion considered in terms of the binding energy per nucleon.

Figure 32.12:   Schematic diagram of a positron emission topography (PET) scanner.

Figure 32.14:   The basic units of matter, starting with a molecule and ending with a quark.

Problems Solved in the Study Guide:
9, 17, 23, 25, 33, 37, 41

Spreadsheets: None

Demonstrations:
Freier and Anderson MPa-1;
Hilton A-22, A-23;
Meiners 41-2.9

Films:
Fusion: The Ultimate Fire, 16mm, color, 14 min., BFA
Atomic Power Production, 16mm, color, 13 min., HFC
Energy: The Nuclear Alternative (Second Edition), 16mm, color, 22 min., CHUH
Fusion: The Electric and Infinite Future, 16mm, color, 22 min., DOC
Learning About Nuclear Energy (Second Edition), 16mm, color, 15 min., EBEC
Nuclear Power: Pro and Con, 16mm, color, 50 min., MCGH
Nuclear Radiation Fallout, 16mm, color, 15 min., CENCO
World of Enrico Fermi, 16mm, b/w, 46 min., HR
Everyday Radioactivity, 16mm, color, 21 min., STERLED
Short-Lived Radioisotopes in Nuclear Medicine, 16mm, color, 27 min., NAVC
Basic Principles of Power Reactors, 16mm, color, 8.5 min., NAVC
Synchrotron, 16mm, color, 14 min., USAEC

Laboratory: None suggested

Computer Resources for Chapter 32

Computer Notes:

CHAPTER 32: LECTURE NOTES
IONIZING RADIATION, NUCLEAR ENERGY, AND ELEMENTARY PARTICLES

Biological Effects of Ionizing Radiation (p. 1008)

Terms and Units Used to Describe Ionizing Radiation

The Effects of Ionizing Radiation on Humans

Induced Nuclear Reactions (p. 1011)

Nuclear Fission (p. 1013)

The Fission Process

Chain Reaction

CHAPTER 32: LECTURE NOTES

Nuclear Reactors (p. 1016)

Basic Components

The Pressurized Water Reactor

Nuclear Fusion (p. 1018)

Nuclear Fusion

Thermonuclear Reactions

Magnetic Confinement

Inertial Confinement

CHAPTER 32: LECTURE NOTES

Elementary Particles (p. 1020)

Setting the Stage

Neutrinos

Positrons and Antiparticles

Muons and Pions

Classification of Particles

Quarks

The Standard Model

CHAPTER 32: NEXT TIME NOTES

PROBLEM LOCATOR GUIDE

The following table is provided for teachers who may wish to know how the homework problems in the third edition correspond to those in the second edition. When using this table, note that the word *new* identifies problems that are new to the third edition and not found in the second edition.

CHAPTER 1   PROBLEM LOCATOR GUIDE

Problem Number		Problem Number		Problem Number	
Physics 3e	*Physics 2e*	*Physics 3e*	*Physics 2e*	*Physics 3e*	*Physics 2e*
1	3	24	48	47	37
2	4	25	19	48	38
3	1	26	20	49	54
4	2	27	22	50 (new)	—
5	47	28	23	51	40
6 (new)	—	29 (new)	—	52	41
7	6	30	24	53	43
8 (new)	—	31	25	54	44
9 (new)	—	32 (new)	—	55	12
10	7	33	27	56 (new)	—
11	8	34	28	57	46
12 (new)	—	35 (new)	—	58	5
13	9	36	29	59	49
14	10	37	30	60	18
15	11	38	31	61	50
16	45	39	32	62 (new)	—
17	13	40	33	63	51
18	14	41 (new)	—	64	52
19	15	42	39	65 (new)	—
20	16	43 (new)	—	66	53
21	17	44	34	67	42
22	21	45	35		
23 (new)	—	46	36		

CHAPTER 2   PROBLEM LOCATOR GUIDE

Problem Number		Problem Number		Problem Number	
Physics 3e	*Physics 2e*	*Physics 3e*	*Physics 2e*	*Physics 3e*	*Physics 2e*
1	3	29	24	57 (new)	—
2	1	30	25	58 (new)	—
3	2	31	26	59	48
4	4	32 (new)	—	60	49
5	5	33	28	61	50
6 (new)	—	34	29	62 (new)	—
7	6	35 (new)	—	63	51
8	7	36	30	64	52
9	8	37	32	65 (new)	—
10 (new)	—	38 (new)	—	66	53
11 (new)	—	39	33	67	54
12	10	40	34	68	37
13	11	41	31	69	56
14	12	42	35	70	57
15 (new)	—	43 (new)	—	71 (new)	—
16	13	44	36	72	58
17	14	45	38	73	59
18	15	46	55	74	60
19	17	47	39	75	61
20 (new)	—	48	40	76	27
21	18	49	41	77	44
22	19	50 (new)	—	78	63
23	20	51	42	79	64
24	16	52	43	80	65
25	21	53	62	81	66
26	22	54	45	82	67
27	23	55	46		
28 (new)	—	56	47		

CHAPTER 3   PROBLEM LOCATOR GUIDE

Problem Number		Problem Number		Problem Number	
Physics 3e	*Physics 2e*	*Physics 3e*	*Physics 2e*	*Physics 3e*	*Physics 2e*
1	1	27	23	53	46
2	2	28	24	54	47
3	3	29	25	55	48
4	4	30	26	56 (new)	—
5	5	31 (new)	—	57	49
6	6	32	21	58	50
7	7	33	28	59 (new)	—
8	8	34	29	60	51
9 (new)	—	35	30	61	52
10	9	36	31	62 (new)	—
11 (new)	—	37	32	63	53
12	10	38	33	64	54
13 (new)	—	39	34	65 (new)	—
14	16	40	35	66	55
15	11	41	36	67	56
16	12	42 (new)	—	68	57
17 (new)	—	43	37	69	58
18	13	44	38	70	59
19	14	45	39	71 (new)	—
20	15	46	40	72	60
21 (new)	—	47	41	73	61
22	17	48	45	74	62
23	18	49	43	75	63
24	19	50	42	76 (new)	—
25	20	51	44	77	64
26	22	52 (new)	—		

CHAPTER 4   PROBLEM LOCATOR GUIDE

Problem Number		Problem Number		Problem Number	
Physics 3e	Physics 2e	Physics 3e	Physics 2e	Physics 3e	Physics 2e
1	3	27	22	53	45
2	2	28 (new)	—	54	46
3	1	29	23	55	43
4 (new)	—	30 (new)	—	56	47
5	4	31	28	57	48
6	5	32	29	58	49
7	6	33 (new)	—	59	50
8	7	34 (new)	—	60 (new)	—
9 (new)	—	35	30	61	51
10	8	36	24	62 (new)	—
11 (new)	—	37	27	63	52
12	10	38	26	64	54
13	11	39	25	65	53
14	9	40	35	66 (new)	—
15	12	41	34	67	55
16 (new)	—	42	33	68	57
17	13	43	36	69 (new)	—
18	14	44	37	70	58
19	16	45	38	71	59
20	17	46 (new)	—	72	60
21	18	47	39	73 (new)	—
22	15	48	40	74	56
23	19	49	41	75	62
24	20	50 (new)	—	76	63
25	21	51 (new)	—	77	64
26 (new)	—	52	44	78	61

CHAPTER 4   CONTINUED

Problem Number		Problem Number		Problem Number	
Physics 3e	Physics 2e	Physics 3e	Physics 2e	Physics 3e	Physics 2e
79	65	92	76	105	87
80	66	93	77	106	88
81	68	94	79	107	90
82	69	95	42	108	91
83	70	96	80	109	92
84	67	97	81	110 (new)	—
85	71	98 (new)	—	111	93
86 (new)	—	99	82	112	89
87	72	100	83	113	94
88	73	101	84	114	95
89 (new)	—	102	78	115 (new)	—
90	74	103	85	116	96
91	75	104	86	117	97

CHAPTER 5   PROBLEM LOCATOR GUIDE

Problem Number		Problem Number		Problem Number	
Physics 3e	Physics 2e	Physics 3e	Physics 2e	Physics3e	Physics 2e
1	1	9 (new)	—	17 (new)	—
2	2	10	9	18	17
3	6	11	11	19	16
4	3	12	12	20	18
5	4	13 (new)	—	21	19
6 (new)	—	14	13	22	20
7	7	15	14	23 (new)	—
8 (new)	—	16	15	24	21

CHAPTER 5   CONTINUED

Problem Number		Problem Number		Problem Number	
Physics 3e	*Physics 2e*	*Physics 3e*	*Physics 2e*	*Physics 3e*	*Physics 2e*
25	22	37	31	48	40
26 (new)	—	38	33	49	26
27	23	39	44	50	42
28 (new)	—	40	34	51	43
29	24	41	35	52	32
30	25	42	36	53	10
31	41	43 (new)	—	54	45
32	27	44	37	55	46
33	28	45 (new)	—	56 (new)	—
34	29	46 (new)	—	57	47
35 (new)	—	47	39	58	48
36	30				

CHAPTER 6   PROBLEM LOCATOR GUIDE

Problem Number		Problem NUmber		Problem Number	
Physics 3e	*Physics 2e*	*Physics 3e*	*Physics 2e*	*Physics 3e*	*Physics 2e*
1	4	10	8	19	16
2	2	11	9	20	17
3 (new)	—	12	10	21	21
4	3	13	13	22	18
5	1	14	11	23 (new)	—
6	5	15	12	24	19
7	6	16	14	25	20
8 (new)	—	17 (new)	—	26 (new)	—
9 (new)	—	18	15	27	24

CHAPTER 6   CONTINUED

Problem Number		Problem Number		Problem Number	
Physics 3e	Physics 2e	Physics 3e	Physics 2e	Physics 3e	Physics 2e
28	22	47	38	66	54
29	23	48 (new)	—	67 (new)	—
30 (new)	—	49	39	68 (new)	—
31	25	50	40	69 (new)	—
32	26	51	41	70 (new)	—
33	27	52	42	71 (new)	—
34	28	53	43	72	55
35	33	54 (new)	—	73 (new)	—
36	29	55 (new)	—	74	56
37	30	56	45	75	57
38 (new)	—	57	46	76	58
39 (new)	—	58	48	77	59
40	32	59	49	78	61
41	34	60	47	79	62
42	35	61	50	80	60
43 (new)	—	62	51	81	63
44	36	63	52	82	64
45	37	64 (new)	—	83	65
46 (new)	—	65	53	84	66

CHAPTER 7   PROBLEM LOCATOR GUIDE

Problem Number		Problem Number		Problem Number	
Physics 3e	*Physics 2e*	*Physics 3e*	*Physics 2e*	*Physics 3e*	*Physics 2e*
1	1	21	18	41	34
2	3	22	19	42	35
3	42	23 (new)	—	43 (new)	—
4	4	24	20	44	36
5	5	25 (new)	—	45 (new)	—
6	6	26	21	46	37
7	7	27	22	47	38
8 (new)	—	28	25	48	2
9	8	29	23	49	39
10	9	30	24	50	40
11	10	31 (new)	—	51	41
12 (new)	—	32	26	52	17
13	11	33	27	53	44
14	12	34	28	54	45
15	13	35 (new)	—	55	46
16	14	36	29	56	47
17	43	37	31	57 (new)	—
18	15	38	30	58	48
19	16	39	32	59	49
20 (new)	—	40	33	60	50

CHAPTER 8   PROBLEM LOCATOR GUIDE

Problem Number		Problem Number		Problem Number	
Physics 3e	Physics 2e	Physics 3e	Physics 2e	Physics 3e	Physics 2e
1	1	26	22	51	41
2 (new)	—	27	23	52	40
3	2	28	3	53	43
4	4	29	24	54 (new)	—
5	6	30	27	55	44
6	7	31 (new)	—	56	45
7	5	32	26	57 (new)	—
8	8	33	25	58	46
9	9	34	28	59 (new)	—
10	11	35 (new)	—	60	47
11	12	36	29	61	48
12	10	37	30	62	50
13	13	38 (new)	—	63	49
14 (new)	—	39	31	64	51
15	14	40	32	65	52
16 (new)	—	41	33	66	53
17	15	42	34	67 (new)	—
18	16	43 (new)	—	68	54
19 (new)	—	44	35	69	55
20	20	45	36	70	56
21	18	46	37	71	57
22	19	47	38	72	58
23	17	48 (new)	—	73 (new)	—
24	21	49	39	74	59
25 (new)	—	50	42		

CHAPTER 9   PROBLEM LOCATOR GUIDE

Problem Number		Problem Number		Problem Number	
Physics 3e	Physics 2e	Physics 3e	Physics 2e	Physics 3e	Physics 2e
1	53	27	22	53	44
2	1	28 (new)	—	54	45
3	3	29	23	55	46
4	2	30	24	56	47
5 (new)	—	31 (new)	—	57 (new)	—
6	4	32	25	58	48
7 (new)	—	33	26	59	49
8	5	34	29	60 (new)	—
9	6	35	27	61	50
10	7	36	28	62	51
11	9	37	30	63 (new)	—
12	8	38	32	64	52
13	10	39	31	65 (new)	—
14 (new)	—	40 (new)	—	66	15
15	11	41	33	67	55
16	12	42	34	68 (new)	—
17	13	43	35	69	56
18	14	44	36	70	57
19	54	45	37	71	58
20	16	46 (new)	—	72	19
21	20	47	38	73	61
22	17	48	39	74	43
23	18	49	40	75	62
24	59	50	42	76	63
25 (new)	—	51	41		
26	21	52	60		

CHAPTER 10   PROBLEM LOCATOR GUIDE

Problem Number		Problem Number		Problem Number	
Physics 3e	*Physics 2e*	*Physics 3e*	*Physics 2e*	*Physics 3e*	*Physics 2e*
1 (new)	—	27	22	53	43
2	62	28	21	54	44
3	2	29	24	55	45
4	3	30	25	56	46
5	4	31	26	57 (new)	—
6	5	32 (new)	—	58	48
7	6	33	27	59	47
8	7	34 (new)	—	60	49
9	8	35	28	61	71
10	9	36	59	62	51
11 (new)	—	37	30	63	52
12	10	38	31	64	53
13	11	39 (new)	—	65	54
14	12	40	32	66 (new)	—
15 (new)	—	41	33	67	55
16	13	42	34	68	56
17 (new)	—	43	35	69	57
18	68	44	36	70	58
19	15	45	37	71	29
20	16	46	38	72 (new)	—
21	17	47	39	73	42
22	18	48 (new)	—	74	1
23	19	49	40	75	64
24	20	50 (new)	—	76	65
25	23	51	41	77	66
26 (new)	—	52	61	78	60

CHAPTER 10　CONTINUED

Problem Number		Problem Number		Problem Number	
Physics 3e	Physics 2e	Physics 3e	Physics 2e	Physics 3e	Physics 2e
79	67	83 (new)	—	87	63
80	14	84	50	88 (new)	—
81	69	85 (new)	—		
82	70	86	72		

CHAPTER 11　PROBLEM LOCATOR GUIDE

Problem Number		Problem Number		Problem Number	
Physics 3e	Physics 2e	Physics 3e	Physics 2e	Physics 3e	Physics 2e
1 (new)	—	18	15	35	28
2	1	19 (new)	—	36	29
3	3	20 (new)	—	37	30
4	2	21	16	38	31
5	4	22	17	39 (new)	—
6 (new)	—	23 (new)	—	40	32
7	5	24	18	41	33
8	6	25	19	42 (new)	—
9	7	26	70	43	35
10	8	27	20	44	36
11 (new)	—	28	22	45	37
12	9	29 (new)	—	46 (new)	—
13	10	30	23	47	38
14	11	31	24	48	39
15	12	32	25	49	40
16	78	33	27	50	41
17	14	34 (new)	—	51 (new)	—

CHAPTER 11 CONTINUED

Problem Number		Problem Number		Problem Number	
Physics 3e	Physics 2e	Physics 3e	Physics 2e	Physics 3e	Physics 2e
52	42	70	58	88	73
53	43	71	82	89	46
54	45	72	59	90	74
55	71	73 (new)	—	91	75
56	44	74	60	92 (new)	—
57	47	75	61	93	76
58 (new)	—	76	62	94	34
59	48	77 (new)	—	95	77
60 (new)	—	78	63	96	79
61	49	79	64	97	13
62	50	80 (new)	—	98	80
63	51	81 (new)	—	99	81
64	68	82	66	100	57
65	53	83	67	101	83
66	54	84	52	102	84
67 (new)	—	85	69	103	85
68	55	86	21		
69	56	87	72		

CHAPTER 12   PROBLEM LOCATOR GUIDE

Problem Number		Problem Number		Problem Number	
Physics 3e	*Physics 2e*	*Physics 3e*	*Physics 2e*	*Physics 3e*	*Physics 2e*
1	1	27	22	53	44
2 (new)	—	28	23	54	45
3	2	29 (new)	—	55	46
4	3	30	72	56	47
5	4	31	27	57	69
6	5	32	25	58	49
7	7	33	26	59	50
8 (new)	—	34	24	60	51
9	6	35	28	61 (new)	—
10	8	36	29	62	52
11	9	37	30	63	53
12	15	38	31	64	55
13	10	39	79	65	54
14	11	40	34	66	56
15	12	41	33	67 (new)	—
16	68	42	35	68	57
17	14	43	36	69	58
18 (new)	—	44	37	70 (new)	—
19	16	45	71	71	59
20	17	46	39	72	60
21	18	47 (new)	—	73	61
22 (new)	—	48	40	74	62
23	19	49	41	75 (new)	—
24	20	50	42	76	63
25 (new)	—	51	43	77	64
26	21	52 (new)	—	78	65

CHAPTER 12   CONTINUED

Problem Number		Problem Number		Problem Number	
Physics 3e	Physics 2e	Physics 3e	Physics 2e	Physics 3e	Physics 2e
79 (new)	—	87 (new)	—	95	80
80	66	88	75	96	81
81	67	89 (new)	—	97	82
82	13	90	77	98	83
83	48	91	74	99 (new)	—
84	70	92	76	100	84
85 (new)	—	93	78		
86	38	94	32		

CHAPTER 13   PROBLEM LOCATOR GUIDE

Problem Number		Problem Number		Problem Number	
Physics 3e	Physics 2e	Physics 3e	Physics 2e	Physics 3e	Physics 2e
1	1	15	12	29	24
2	26	16	13	30	25
3	2	17	14	31	30
4	4	18	27	32	15
5 (new)	—	19	16	33	8
6	5	20	17	34	18
7	6	21	28	35	29
8 (new)	—	22	19	36 (new)	—
9	9	23	20	37	31
10 (new)	—	24	21	38 (new)	—
11	10	25 (new)	—	39	32
12 (new)	—	26	22	40	33
13	11	27	23	41	34
14 (new)	—	28 (new)	—	42 (new)	—

CHAPTER 14   PROBLEM LOCATOR GUIDE

Problem Number		Problem Number		Problem Number	
Physics 3e	*Physics 2e*	*Physics 3e*	*Physics 2e*	*Physics 3e*	*Physics 2e*
1	1	22	18	43	36
2	2	23 (new)	—	44	37
3	42	24	22	45	38
4 (new)	—	25	21	46	39
5	4	26 (new)	—	47 (new)	—
6	6	27	23	48	9
7	5	28	24	49	14
8	7	29 (new)	—	50	3
9	8	30	25	51 (new)	—
10	40	31	26	52	43
11	10	32 (new)	—	53	30
12 (new)	—	33	27	54 (new)	—
13	11	34	28	55	45
14	12	35 (new)	—	56	46
15	13	36	44	57 (new)	—
16	41	37	31	58	48
17	15	38	32	59	47
18	16	39 (new)	—	60	49
19	17	40	34	61	50
20	20	41	33		
21 (new)	—	42	35		

CHAPTER 15   PROBLEM LOCATOR GUIDE

Problem Number		Problem Number		Problem Number	
Physics 3e	Physics 2e	Physics 3e	Physics 2e	Physics 3e	Physics 2e
1	1	27	24	53	74
2	2	28	25	54	47
3	67	29	26	55	48
4	4	30	17	56 (new)	—
5 (new)	—	31	27	57	49
6	5	32	28	58 (new)	—
7	6	33	29	59 (new)	—
8 (new)	—	34	30	60	50
9	69	35	31	61	51
10	9	36 (new)	—	62	52
11	11	37	32	63	70
12	10	38	33	64	54
13	12	39	80	65	55
14	13	40	35	66	56
15	15	41	36	67	58
16	14	42	37	68 (new)	—
17	16	43	39	69	57
18 (new)	—	44	38	70	59
19 (new)	—	45	41	71	60
20	18	46	40	72 (new)	—
21	19	47 (new)	—	73 (new)	—
22	20	48	42	74	61
23	66	49 (new)	—	75	62
24	22	50	43	76 (new)	—
25	23	51	44	77	63
26 (new)	—	52	45	78	64

CHAPTER 15   CONTINUED

Problem Number		Problem Number		Problem Number	
Physics 3e	Physics 2e	Physics 3e	Physics 2e	Physics 3e	Physics 2e
79	65	86	72	93	78
80	21	87	73	94	82
81	3	88	46	95	34
82	68	89	75	96	81
83	8	90	76	97	79
84	53	91	77	98 (new)	—
85	71	92 (new)	—		

CHAPTER 16   PROBLEM LOCATOR GUIDE

Problem Number		Problem Number		Problem Number	
Physics 3e	Physics 2e	Physics 3e	Physics 2e	Physics 3e	Physics 2e
1	1	14	13	27	21
2	2	15 (new)	—	28	25
3 (new)	—	16	15	29 (new)	—
4	3	17	16	30	26
5	77	18	70	31	27
6	5	19	17	32	30
7	6	20	18	33	31
8	7	21	19	34	69
9	8	22 (new)	—	35 (new)	—
10	9	23	20	36	33
11	10	24	23	37	28
12	11	25	75	38	34
13	12	26	24	39	36

CHAPTER 16   CONTINUED

Problem Number		Problem Number		Problem Number	
Physics 3e	Physics 2e	Physics 3e	Physics 2e	Physics 3e	Physics 2e
40	29	63	52	86	67
41	35	64	53	87	68
42	37	65 (new)	—	88	32
43 (new)	—	66	54	89 (new)	—
44	38	67 (new)	—	90	14
45	39	68	55	91	71
46 (new)	—	69	56	92	72
47	40	70 (new)	—	93 (new)	—
48 (new)	—	71	57	94	46
49	41	72	58	95	74
50	42	73 (new)	—	96	22
51	43	74	59	97	76
52	44	75	60	98	4
53 (new)	—	76 (new)	—	99	78
54	45	77	61	100 (new)	—
55	73	78	63	101	79
56 (new)	—	79	62	102	80
57	47	80 (new)	—	103	81
58	48	81	64	104	82
59 (new)	—	82 (new)	—	105	83
60	49	83	65	106	85
61	50	84 (new)	—	107	84
62	51	85	66	108 (new)	—

CHAPTER 17   PROBLEM LOCATOR GUIDE

Problem Number		Problem Number		Problem Number	
Physics 3e	*Physics 2e*	*Physics 3e*	*Physics 2e*	*Physics 3e*	*Physics 2e*
1 (new)	—	22	17	43	34
2 (new)	—	23 (new)	—	44 (new)	—
3	3	24	48	45	46
4	43	25	19	46	36
5	5	26	20	47	37
6 (new)	—	27	23	48	38
7 (new)	—	28	24	49	49
8	7	29	21	50	40
9 (new)		30	22	51 (new)	—
10 (new)	—	31 (new)	—	52	30
11	8	32	25	53	4
12	9	33 (new)	—	54	16
13	10	34	26	55 (new)	—
14 (new)	—	35	27	56	35
15	11	36 (new)	—	57	47
16 (new)	—	37	28	58 (new)	—
17	12	38	29	59	39
18	13	39	42	60	18
19	14	40	31	61	50
20	44	41	32		
21	15	42	33		

CHAPTER 18   PROBLEM LOCATOR GUIDE

Problem Number		Problem Number		Problem Number	
Physics 3e	*Physics 2e*	*Physics 3e*	*Physics 2e*	*Physics 3e*	*Physics 2e*
1	1	25	20	49 (new)	—
2	2	26	21	50 (new)	—
3	3	27	22	51 (new)	—
4	4	28	23	52 (new)	—
5	5	29 (new)	—	53 (new)	—
6 (new)	—	30	38	54 (new)	—
7	6	31	25	55 (new)	—
8 (new)	—	32	26	56 (new)	—
9	7	33	27	57	9
10	8	34 (new)	—	58 (new)	—
11	37	35	28	59	24
12	10	36	29	60	39
13	41	37 (new)	—	61	40
14 (new)	—	38 (new)	—	62 (new)	—
15	12	39	31	63	11
16	13	40 (new)	—	64	42
17	14	41	32	65	43
18	15	42 (new)	—	66	44
19	16	43	33	67 (new)	—
20 (new)	—	44	34	68	17
21	45	45	35	69	46
22	18	46 (new)	—	70 (new)	—
23 (new)	—	47	36	71	47
24	19	48 (new)	—		

CHAPTER 19   PROBLEM LOCATOR GUIDE

Problem Number		Problem Number		Problem Number	
Physics 3e	*Physics 2e*	*Physics 3e*	*Physics 2e*	*Physics 3e*	*Physics 2e*
1	1	23 (new)	—	45	49
2	3	24	20	46	39
3	4	25	21	47	40
4	2	26	22	48	41
5	5	27	23	49	42
6	6	28	24	50	51
7 (new)	—	29 (new)	—	51	44
8	8	30	25	52	45
9 (new)	—	31	26	53 (new)	—
10	9	32	27	54	13
11 (new)	—	33	29	55 (new)	—
12	10	34	28	56	7
13	11	35	30	57	35
14	12	36 (new)	—	58	48
15	46	37	31	59	38
16	14	38 (new)	—	60	50
17 (new)	—	39	32	61 (new)	—
18	15	40	34	62	43
19	16	41	47	63	52
20	17	42	36	64 (new)	—
21	18	43	33	65	53
22	19	44	37	66	54

CHAPTER 20   PROBLEM LOCATOR GUIDE

Problem Number		Problem Number		Problem Number	
Physics 3e	Physics 2e	Physics 3e	Physics 2e	Physics 3e	Physics 2e
1	95	27	24	52 (new)	—
2	2	28	25	53	45
3	4	29 (new)	—	54	46
4	5	30	26	55	47
5	6	31	27	56 (new)	—
6	3	32	28	57	48
7	7			58	49
8	8	33	29	59	50
9 (new)	—	34	31	60 (new)	—
10	9	35	30	61	51
11	10	36 (new)	—	62	52
12	11	37	32	63	53
13	12	38	33	64	54
14	13	39 (new)	—	65	55
15 (new)	—	40	34	66 (new)	—
16	14	41	35	67	56
17	15	42	36	68	57
18	16	43	37	69	58
19 (new)	—	44	38	70	59
20	17	45	39	71	60
21	18	46 (new)	—	72	61
22	19	47	40	73	62
23	21	48	41	74	63
24	22	49	42	75	64
25	94	50	43	76	65
26	20	51	44	77 (new)	—

CHAPTER 20   CONTINUED

Problem Number		Problem Number		Problem Number	
Physics 3e	Physics 2e	Physics 3e	Physics 2e	Physics 3e	Physics 2e
78	66	93	93	108	68
79	67	94	81	109	97
80	96	95	83	110 (new)	—
81	69	96	84	111	74
82	70	97	85	112	99
83	71	98	86	113	101
84	72	99	87	114	102
85	98	100	88	115	103
86	75	101	89	116	100
87	73	102	90	117	104
88	76	103	91	118	105
89	77	104	92	119	106
90	78	105	80	120	107
91	82	106	23	121	108
92	79	107	1	122	109

CHAPTER 21   PROBLEM LOCATOR GUIDE

Problem Number		Problem Number		Problem Number	
Physics 3e	Physics 2e	Physics 3e	Physics 2e	Physics 3e	Physics 2e
1	1	7 (new)	—	13	10
2	2	8 (new)	—	14	9
3	4	9	7	15	12
4	5	10 (new)	—	16	13
5	53	11	8	17 (new)	—
6	6	12	11	18	14

CHAPTER 21   CONTINUED

Problem Number		Problem Number		Problem Number	
Physics 3e	Physics 2e	Physics 3e	Physics 2e	Physics 3e	Physics 2e
19	15	41	34	63 (new)	—
20	16	42	36	64	52
21	17	43	37	65 (new)	—
22	20	44	35	66 (new)	—
23 (new)	—	45 (new)	—	67 (new)	—
24	18	46 (new)	—	68 (new)	—
25	19	47 (new)	—	69	3
26	21	48	38	70	54
27 (new)	—	49	39	71	33
28	23	50	40	72	56
29	24	51	41	73	57
30 (new)	—	52	43	74	26
31	25	53	44	75	59
32	58	54	42	76	60
33	27	55 (new)	—	77	61
34	28	56	45	78	62
35	29	57	46	79 (new)	—
36 (new)	—	58	47	80	63
37	30	59	50	81	64
38	31	60	51	82	22
39	32	61	48	83	66
40	55	62	49		

CHAPTER 22　PROBLEM LOCATOR GUIDE

Problem Number		Problem Number		Problem Number	
Physics 3e	*Physics 2e*	*Physics 3e*	*Physics 2e*	*Physics 3e*	*Physics 2e*
1	1	28	22	55 (new)	—
2	2	29	58	56	47
3	3	30	24	57 (new)	—
4	4	31	25	58	48
5 (new)	—	32	26	59 (new)	—
6	5	33	27	60	49
7 (new)	—	34	28	61	50
8	7	35	29	62	51
9	6	36	30	63	52
10	8	37	31	64	53
11	9	38	32	65	54
12	10	39	33	66	55
13	11	40 (new)	—	67	17
14 (new)	—	41	34	68	57
15	12	42	35	69	23
16	13	43	61	70 (new)	—
17 (new)	—	44	37	71	59
18	14	45	38	72	60
19 (new)	—	46	39	73	36
20	15	47	40	74 (new)	—
21	16	48	41	75	62
22	56	49 (new)	—	76	64
23	18	50	42	77	65
24	19	51	43	78	63
25	21	52	44	79	66
26 (new)	—	53	45	80	67
27	20	54	46		

CHAPTER 23   PROBLEM LOCATOR GUIDE

Problem Number		Problem Number		Problem Number	
Physics 3e	Physics 2e	Physics 3e	Physics 2e	Physics 3e	Physics 2e
1	1	18	14	35	28
2	2	19 (new)	—	36	29
3	3	20	15	37	30
4	35	21	17	38	32
5	5	22	18	39	33
6	6	23	16	40	34
7 (new)	—	24	19	41	4
8 (new)	—	25 (new)	—	42 (new)	—
9	7	26	20	43	36
10	8	27	21	44	37
11 (new)	—	28	22	45	27
12	9	29	23	46 (new)	—
13	10	30	24	47	40
14	11	31 (new)	—	48	31
15	12	32	25	49	39
16 (new)	—	33	26	50 (new)	—
17	13	34	38	51	41

CHAPTER 24   PROBLEM LOCATOR GUIDE

Problem Number		Problem Number		Problem Number	
Physics 3e	Physics 2e	Physics 3e	Physics 2e	Physics 3e	Physics 2e
1	35	6 (new)	—	11	9
2	2	7	6	12	33
3	3	8	7	13 (new)	—
4	4	9 (new)	—	14	11
5	5	10	8	15	12

CHAPTER 24   CONTINUED

Problem Number		Problem Number		Problem Number	
Physics 3e	*Physics 2e*	*Physics 3e*	*Physics 2e*	*Physics 3e*	*Physics 2e*
16 (new)	—	30	23	44	21
17	13	31	24	45	1
18	14	32	25	46	36
19 (new)	—	33 (new)	—	47 (new)	—
20	15	34	38	48	37
21	16	35	27	49	26
22	17	36	28	50	39
23	18	37	29	51	40
24	19	38	30	52	41
25 (new)	—	39 (new)	—	53	42
26	20	40	31	54 (new)	—
27	34	41	32	55	43
28 (new)	—	42	10	56	44
29	22	43 (new)	—		

CHAPTER 25   PROBLEM LOCATOR GUIDE

Problem Number		Problem Number		Problem Number	
Physics 3e	*Physics 2e*	*Physics 3e*	*Physics 2e*	*Physics 3e*	*Physics 2e*
1	1	8	8	15 (new)	—
2	2	9 (new)	—	16	13
3	3	10	9	17	14
4 (new)	—	11	10	18	15
5	4	12 (new)	—	19 (new)	—
6	5	13	11	20	16
7	33	14	12	21	17

CHAPTER 25   CONTINUED

Problem Number		Problem Number		Problem Number	
Physics 3e	Physics 2e	Physics 3e	Physics 2e	Physics 3e	Physics 2e
22	29	30	27	38	7
23	19	31	28	39	24
24	21	32	18	40	34
25	22	33	20	41 (new)	—
26 (new)	—	34	30	42	35
27	23	35	31	43	36
28	26	36 (new)	—		
29 (new)	—	37	32		

CHAPTER 26   PROBLEM LOCATOR GUIDE

Problem Number		Problem Number		Problem Number	
Physics 3e	Physics 2e	Physics 3e	Physics 2e	Physics 3e	Physics 2e
1	1	14 (new)	—	27	25
2	3	15	13	28 (new)	—
3	2	16	90	29	26
4	4	17	15	30	24
5	5	18	16	31	27
6	6	19	17	32	28
7	7	20	19	33	29
8	8	21	18	34	31
9	9	22 (new)	—	35	30
10	10	23	20	36 (new)	—
11	11	24	21	37	32
12	12	25	23	38	33
13 (new)	—	26	22	39 (new)	—

CHAPTER 26   CONTINUED

Problem Number		Problem Number		Problem Number	
Physics 3e	Physics 2e	Physics 3e	Physics 2e	Physics 3e	Physics 2e
40	34	68	57	96	82
41	35	69 (new)	—	97	95
42	36	70	58	98	85
43	37	71	60	99	86
44	38	72	59	100	87
45 (new)	—	73	61	101	41
46	39	74	62	102	76
47	40	75	91	103	14
48	88	76	64	104 (new)	—
49	42	77	65	105	63
50 (new)	—	78	66	106	99
51	43	79	67	107	92
52	44	80	68	108	93
53	45	81 (new)	—	109 (new)	—
54	100	82	94	110	69
55	47	83	70	111	83
56	48	84	71	112	96
57 (new)	—	85	72	113	97
58	50	86	73	114	98
59	51	87	74	115	46
60	49	88	75	116	101
61	52	89	89	117	102
62	53	90	77	118	103
63 (new)	—	91	78	119	104
64 (new)	—	92	79	120	105
65	54	93	84	121	106
66	55	94	80	122 (new)	—
67	56	95	81	123	107

CHAPTER 27   PROBLEM LOCATOR GUIDE

Problem Number		Problem Number		Problem Number	
Physics 3e	*Physics 2e*	*Physics 3e*	*Physics 2e*	*Physics 3e*	*Physics 2e*
1 (new)	—	23	20	45	36
2	1	24	19	46 (new)	—
3	44	25	17	47	37
4	3	26	22	48	38
5	4	27 (new)	—	49	40
6	5	28	21	50	39
7	51	29 (new)	—	51	41
8	6	30	23	52	42
9	7	31	26	53	2
10 (new)	—	32	24	54 (new)	—
11 (new)	—	33	25	55	45
12	11	34	27	56	46
13	13	35 (new)	—	57	47
14	9	36	28	58	43
15	10	37 (new)	—	59	48
16	12	38	30	60 (new)	—
17	49	39	31	61	50
18	15	40 (new)	—	62	8
19	14	41	32	63	52
20	16	42	33	64	53
21	18	43	34		
22 (new)	—	44	35		

CHAPTER 28   PROBLEM LOCATOR GUIDE

Problem Number		Problem Number		Problem Number	
Physics 3e	*Physics 2e*	*Physics 3e*	*Physics 2e*	*Physics 3e*	*Physics 2e*
1	1	17	13	33	24
2	31	18 (new)	—	34	25
3	3	19	14	35	26
4	4	20	15	36	27
5 (new)	—	21 (new)	—	37	28
6	5	22	33	38	29
7	6	23	17	39	21
8	7	24	18	40	2
9 (new)	—	25	19	41	32
10	8	26 (new)	—	42	16
11 (new)	—	27	20	43	34
12 (new)	—	28	30	44	35
13	10	29 (new)	—	45 (new)	—
14 (new)	—	30	22	46	36
15	11	31	23	47	37
16	12	32 (new)	—		

CHAPTER 29   PROBLEM LOCATOR GUIDE

Problem Number		Problem Number		Problem Number	
Physics 3e	*Physics 2e*	*Physics 3e*	*Physics 2e*	*Physics 3e*	*Physics 2e*
1	1	6	5	11	10
2	33	7	36	12	38
3	3	8	7	13	12
4	4	9	8	14	13
5 (new)	—	10	9	15	14

CHAPTER 29   CONTINUED

Problem Number		Problem Number		Problem Number	
Physics 3e	Physics 2e	Physics 3e	Physics 2e	Physics 3e	Physics 2e
16 (new)	—	27	22	38	30
17	15	28	23	39	32
18	16	29 (new)	—	40	2
19	17	30	24	41	34
20	18	31	25	42 (new)	—
21 (new)	—	32	26	43	35
22 (new)	—	33 (new)	—	44	6
23	19	34	27	45	37
24	20	35	28	46	11
25 (new)	—	36	29	47	39
26	21	37	31	48	40

CHAPTER 30   PROBLEM LOCATOR GUIDE

Problem Number		Problem Number		Problem Number	
Physics 3e	Physics 2e	Physics 3e	Physics 2e	Physics 3e	Physics 2e
1 (new)	—	11	13	21	19
2	2	12	10	22 (new)	—
3	3	13	11	23	20
4 (new)	—	14 (new)	—	24	21
5	4	15	12	25	22
6	5	16	14	26	23
7	6	17	15	27	25
8	7	18	16	28	24
9	8	19	48	29 (new)	—
10	41	20	18	30	26

CHAPTER 30   CONTINUED

Problem Number		Problem Number		Problem Number	
Physics 3e	*Physics 2e*	*Physics 3e*	*Physics 2e*	*Physics 3e*	*Physics 2e*
31	39	41 (new)	—	51	43
32	28	42	35	52	44
33	29	43	36	53 (new)	—
34 (new)	—	44	37	54	45
35	30	45	38	55	46
36	31	46 (new)	—	56	47
37	32	47	27	57	17
38 (new)	—	48	40	58	49
39	33	49	9	59	50
40	34	50	42		

CHAPTER 31   PROBLEM LOCATOR GUIDE

Problem Number		Problem Number		Problem Number	
Physics 3e	*Physics 2e*	*Physics 3e*	*Physics 2e*	*Physics 3e*	*Physics 2e*
1	43	12 (new)	—	23 (new)	—
2	2	13	10	24	19
3	3	14	11	25	46
4	4	15	12	26	23
5 (new)	—	16	13	27	21
6	5	17 (new)	—	28	24
7	6	18	14	29	22
8 (new)	—	19	15	30	25
9	7	20	16	31	26
10	8	21	17	32	28
11	9	22	44	33	27

CHAPTER 31   CONTINUED

Problem Number		Problem Number		Problem Number	
Physics 3e	Physics 2e	Physics 3e	Physics 2e	Physics 3e	Physics 2e
34 (new)	—	43	36	52	18
35	29	44	37	53	45
36	30	45 (new)	—	54	20
37	33	46	38	55 (new)	—
38	49	47	39	56	47
39	32	48	40	57	48
40	34	49	41	58	31
41 (new)	—	50	42	59	50
42	35	51	1	60	51

CHAPTER 32   PROBLEM LOCATOR GUIDE

Problem Number		Problem Number		Problem Number	
Physics 3e	Physics 2e	Physics 3e	Physics 2e	Physics 3e	Physics 2e
1	1	13	10	25	21
2 (new)	—	14	11	26 (new)	—
3	4	15	12	27	23
4	3	16	13	28	24
5 (new)	—	17 (new)	—	29	25
6	5	18	14	30 (new)	—
7	6	19	15	31	26
8	7	20	16	32	27
9 (new)	—	21	17	33	28
10	8	22	38	34	41
11	9	23	19	35 (new)	—
12 (new)	—	24	20	36 (new)	—

CHAPTER 32   CONTINUED

Problem Number		Problem Number		Problem Number	
Physics 3e	Physics 2e	Physics 3e	Physics 2e	Physics 3e	Physics 2e
37 (new)	—	43	35	49 (new)	—
38 (new)	—	44	36	50	22
39	30	45	37	51	43
40	31	46	18	52	44
41	33	47	39		
42	34	48	40